HOW TO
BUILD & OPERATE YOUR OWN SMALL HYDROELECTRIC PLANT

D1453381

HOW TO
BUILD & OPERATE YOUR OWN SMALL HYDROELECTRIC PLANT

BY J. GEORGE BUTLER

TAB BOOKS Inc.
BLUE RIDGE SUMMIT, PA. 17214

All photos are by George and June Butler unless otherwise credited.

FIRST EDITION

SECOND PRINTING

Copyright © 1982 by TAB BOOKS Inc.

Printed in the United States of America

Library of Congress Cataloging in Publication Data

Butler, J. George.
    How to build and operate your own small
hydroelectric plant.

    Includes index.
    1. Hydroelectric power plants—Amateurs'
manuals. I. Title.
TK1081.B87   62.31′2134   81-18278
ISBN 0-8306-0065-5   AACR2
ISBN 0-8306-1417-6 (pbk.)

Contents

Preface

Russell Conwell was a Civil War Colonel, Boston Barrister, Baptist preacher, and the founder and first president of Temple University in Philadelphia. I vividly remember my father taking me as a small boy to hear Conwell give his "Acres of Diamonds" lecture, a talk he gave over 6,000 times.

The thread of the lecture was always the same. Conwell believed there were acres of diamonds to be found in everyone's back yard, if one but only looked for them.

The never-varying heart of the lecture was about Ali Hafed, an ancient Persian who lived near the Indus River. Ali was rich. He owned a large farm with a beautiful brook running through it. Ali was contented, contented that is until an old Buddhist priest came to see him. The priest told him about diamonds. Then Ali was discontented; he wanted diamonds and he wanted to be richer.

So Ali sold his farm and set out to find diamonds. He first searched at the Mountains of the Moon and then through Palestine and Europe. At last, when his money was spent and he was in rags, wretched, and completely broken, he searched on the shores of the Mediterranean in Spain. It was there that a great tidal wave rolled in from the Gates of Hercules. Ali flung himself into it and disappeared beneath the foaming crest, never to rise again.

The man who purchased Ali's farm was revisited one day by the same old priest. The moment the priest entered, he saw a flash of light from the mantel. He rushed up to it and shouted, "This is a diamond. Has Ali Hafed returned?"

"Oh no," said the new owner, "Ali has not returned and that is not a diamond. It is just a stone I found in the garden brook."

"But I tell you, I know a diamond when I see one," said the priest. "This is a diamond."

Together the two men rushed out and into the stream where Ali had so often watered his camel. As they stirred up the white sands of the brook with their fingers, they found stones more beautiful and valuable than the first. Thus was discovered the Golconda diamond mine, the most magnificent diamond mine in the history of mankind, excelling even the Kimberly.

Conwell died in 1925, yet the truth of his "acres of diamonds" still lives. It is true for America as a whole. It is particularly true for New England where only 7 percent of its present electricity comes from the falling water that once made the region preeminent in manufacturing. My own experience confirms it. America has the resources to overcome its present energy problems, if we have the will to use them.

Several years ago, the late David E. Lilienthal, the "grand old man" of the TVA" and the first chairman of the atomic Energy Commission, made an impassioned plea for hydroelectric development in America.

Lilienthal estimated America's undeveloped hydro potential to be twice that which was developed, if we just used the 50,000 dams 25 feet and higher that were presently standing, unused. Yet this estimate, taken from the old Federal Power Commission's (now the Federal Energy Regulatory Commission) statistics only included sites capable of producing 5,000 kilowatts or more. Smaller sites, which abound in America as elsewhere in the world, were not considered, nor were any tidal projects mentioned, such as Cook's Inlet, Alaska, or Passamaquoddy in Maine, whose potential power production boggles the mind. As much water flows into the Bay of Fundy on one tide as flows down the

Mississippi above New Orleans in two weeks, an amount equal to that from a drainage area half that of the continental United States.

On my farm is a beautiful mountain brook. Once it powered a small sawmill, the stone work of which still stands. Why shouldn't I "think small" I wondered. I contemplated the oil and electricity I would save, if I could turn the mechanical energy of falling water into electrical energy. By using modern technology, I would rediscover a resource which once made New England great. I found I could provide heat and light for my farm, as well as sell my surplus "power" to a utility to help others less fortunately situated.

Acknowledgments

Many people significantly contributed to my endeavors. In particular I am deeply indebted to:

Dr. R. Stevens Kleinschmidt, one of America's foremost hydroelectric engineers. Under his guidance, I undertook the innovative installation of my hydroelectric plant. That it resulted in the great success it turned out to be ("A textbook illustration of how to build a small hydro plant," as the Chairman of Vermont's Public Service Board characterized it) is due entirely to Steve. Together we have demonstrated that an ordinary centrifugal pump, which is relatively inexpensive because it is mass produced, can serve as a turbine, and when run backwards, can turn an induction mill motor, and automatically produce 60 cycle power without any other regulatory equipment with just about the same efficiency as a Pelton wheel.

Robert T. Stafford and Patrick J. Leahy, Vermont's two United States senators, who responded to my many requests for information with great good will and efficiency and who provided U.S. Government statistical data.

James D. Hebson, an official of the old Federal Power Commission, for patiently answering my questions.

The Army Corps of Engineers, New England Division.

Department of Energy, Region I Office, Boston, and in particular to Karen Klam for her prompt and complete responses to my queries.

The librarians at the Southeastern Regional Library.

The Brooks Memorial Library in Brattleboro, Vermont.

Don Webster, owner of CBS radio station WKVT, for calling my attention to and providing me with a tape of the Osgood File from CBS.

Charles Komanoff and Dr. Vince Taylor for their valuable technical studies.

Cecil Thrash, manager of public relations for the Worthington Group of McGraw Edison.

Larry Shafer, marketing manager for Hydro Power and Water Supply, at Worthington's Engineering Division, Taneytown, Maryland.

Richard Plumber and George Watts of Dartmouth College for Exhibiting Dartmouth's co-generation power plant to me.

Granite State Electric, New England Power, and the New England Electric System for supplying photographs of various processes and for giving me permission to take additional ones.

Bill Wocjik at the Vernon hydro station.

Hugh Sullivan, in charge of New England Electric's six dams on the Connecticut.

Dr. Harold Knapp, formerly with the AEC and now vindicated in his findings of the radiation poisoning of 4,000 sheep at the atomic blasts in the early 1950s.

Georgetown University for a tour of its new powerplant.

Glenn Lovin, Chairman, Internation Co-generation Society.

Edison Electric Institute.

Officials of Utah Power and Light.

Don Tufts of Pineville, Louisiana, a friend of many years, for his information on International Paper Company's co-generation.

Hervey Scudder of Brattleboro, Vermont, formerly with Lilienthal's Development and Resource Corporation and now a hydro consultant at his Hydropower Development Center.

William S. White, Chairman and Chief Executive Officer, American Electric Power for information on AEP's pressurized, fluidized bed combustion of coal.

John White of the State Energy Office, Vermont, one of those unsung heroes who works diligently, efficiently, and sacrificially for the public good.

André Rouleau, a state official and formerly of the State Water Resources Board, who is now environmental engineering supervisor for the State of Vermont.

Ralph Dickinson of Heath Massachusetts for help with precipitation data, which he has kept for 14 years for the Massachusetts Department of Natural Resources.

Frances Ross, for introducing me to the Washington Spectator and for providing me with a key copy.

Harry McKay of McKay Water Power Limited, Port Colborne, Ontario, who first introduced me to Steve Kleinschmidt.

The Vermont Electric Cooperative for its help along the way in becoming the first co-generator on its lines.

When "Murphy's Law" showed its power, where would I have been without newfound friends such as Gene Claussen?

Neal Houston, Senator Robert Stafford's Administrative Assistant, as well as the many government clerks who were helpful.

Every individual and company who provided permission to use material from their books including Lelan F. Sillin, Jr., President of Northeast Utilities; Westinghouse; General Electric; Reliance Electric Co.; the Department of Energy and its National Center for Appropriate Technology, Otisca Industries Ltd., Hydro Quebec; the Goodheart-Willcox Co.; the War Resisters League, and the Worthington Pump Corp.

Howard M. "Bud" Bemis and his sons Randy and Rodney. Bud's specialized expertise saved countless hours of trial and error in laying 2700 feet of penstock through the Vermont woods without blasting. It is unusual for a backhoe man to have and use a transit, but Bud is an unusual man. His generosity in letting me use his old 4 wheel drive truck was greatly appreciated. Randy's suggestion of sowing winter rye to get vegetation growing immediately to prevent erosion was typical of the practicality of both him and his brother and father. Rod's expertise as a lineman, his cheerful good humor, and his mechanical and electrical skills contributed greatly to the work. To Bud and his boys, I give my deepest thanks.

Ernest Behrens, Larry Crosier, Fred Crosby, Ray Boyd, my neighbors, They helped in many ways: keeping equipment running, supplying various components, and all exhibiting that quality of neighborliness so cherished in time of need. To them all, I give my sincere thanks.

The many friends who supplied invaluable clippings from their hometown newspapers. In particular I am indebted to my sister and brother-in-law, Dr. and Mrs. Walter A. Luszki of Charleston, South Carolina for timely items from the *Charleston News* and *Courier*.

Percy Dodge, Village Blacksmith, now 81 and still making the sparks fly and the anvil ring, for his help in fashioning the trash rack, cutting pipe, fixing channel iron, etc. Paul Dary, the village plumber, was also very helpful.

My wife June, who stood by through the entire process, took pictures, and made drawings.

Unfortunately, space does not permit mentioning so many others, whose help I have deeply appreciated.

Introduction

This book is primarily an account of how I harnessed my brook. No two situations are identical, however, and neither I nor Dr. Kleinschmidt can assume responsibility for persons undertaking similar projects. This book is intended as a general guide.

The uniqueness of this method lies in its marriage of two techniques which have been used separately in the past. This uniqueness lies also in applying the idea of a pump as a turbine to a small hydro, making many such installations economically practical.

Professional help is strongly recommended for the layman undertaking this kind of project. Electricity can be a deadly killer. So too, can uncontrolled water pressure from such high head installations as this. Each must be handled properly, with adequate precautions to ensure safety. With proper precautions and professional oversight, these innovative concepts can be of great value. In the bibliography at the end of this work I have suggested references for additional information which in turn suggest engineering firms which may be helpful.

Chapter 1

They Said It Couldn't Be Done

They said it couldn't be done! Everyone with whom I talked, discouraged me. Maybe it was just my "cussedness" as one luminary at the dedication of the project called it. At any rate, I was challenged by the perennial refrain.

I knew little of the technical part of electricity. College physics was a dim blur in the distant past. But I could learn. And I was not afraid of work. Harnessing swift flowing streams had once made New England great. Why not "think small" and re-use the myriad small waterways that were everywhere? New England, the entire Appalachian chain in the east, the mountains of the west, the Piedmont, or hill country anywhere, all provide excellent possibilities for harnessing water power.

We bought our Vermont farm in 1954. One of the reasons we bought it was that it had two streams. One, the North River, once had half a dozen mills on it in a dozen miles between Jacksonville, Vermont, and Colrain, Massachusetts.

The cascading brook that ran down from the mountain behind the 18th century farmhouse had not been overlooked either by those early settlers in their search for energy. The stone work (Fig. 1-1) showed where the old mill had stood. Its crib dam had long since crumbled. A canal or flume lead the

Fig. 1-1. Stone work of 19th century sawmill on brook which piqued my interest in the possibility of harnessing this brook with modern technology.

water to the mill, as evidenced by the stone foundation a hundred yards downstream. Here was mute evidence to the ingenuity and imagination that permeated New England in the past century.

Perhaps I was conditioned to "think hydro" by my early childhood. I am one of those rare museum pieces, who not only was born in Washington, D.C., but whose parents were also born there. My parents were accustomed to seek surcease from the fetid, humid atmosphere of "Foggy Bottom" each August for a few glorious weeks in the Valley of Virginia. In those years of World War I, and after in the 1920s many of the old grist mills had already been abandoned. The photographs by my father of the old mill near Rock Enon Springs, Virginia, itself now long gone, show how "progress" had treated one of these relics even then. Figures 1-2 and 1-3 show an abandoned grist mill, near Rock Enon Springs Virginia, 18 miles west of Winchester, Virginia. These photos were taken by my father, the Rev. C.H. Butler. Even then, time was destroying the giant wheel. The flume was dilapidated, and the forest growth was quickly taking over where man had once worked.

In the Page Valley near Luray, Virginia, in the 1920s, two other grist mills, one on the Hawksbill Creek, another on the Shenandoah River, were still operating. "Progress" did

Fig. 1-2. "Down by the old mill stream." The America that was. An old mill in the Great North Mountains of Virginia, near Rock Enon Springs, Virginia. The latter, a favorite watering spa in the 1880s and 1890s, has now vanished along with the mill and post office. Such mills are relics of an America now long gone.

Fig. 1-3. This is another view of the old mill near Rock Enon Springs, Virginia. Both of these photographs were taken in August of 1918.

not catch up to them until the World War II era. Now, both of them are in ruins.

HOW I DISCOVERED THE WAY TO GO

Ever since we became country people, I started looking for a way to harness the water on the farm. Each spring, as I tapped my sugar maples and gathered the sap, I heard the lambent voice of the brook as it flowed through the sugar bush, singing a song which to my ears said: "kilowatts, kilowatts."

Being a disciple of Tom Sawyer, I subscribed to his thesis: work consists in what one is obliged to do; play, is what one is not obliged to do. I inveigled as many friends as possible to participate in the "play" of gathering maple sap in the clean, crisp mountain air and untrammeled snow of the Vermont woods in early spring. One friend, an insurance executive from Hartford, Connecticut, luxuriating in the glory of nature, exclaimed: "You ought to charge $20 a day just for the privilege of being in the woods." (This was when $20 was worth $20!)

I suggested that I would gladly oblige him if he wished. Unfortunately for this Sawyerite, he didn't wish! But another friend made an even better suggestion. He was an electrician. He thought a simple water wheel would be easy to make from an old cable drum, fitted with paddles, approximating the old overshot wheels of my childhood.

Though later I was to learn that the efficiency of this type of wheel did not begin to approach that of a Pelton wheel. I was motivated by his suggestion to look further into the possibilities of using this renewable resource.

Another friend, a competent civil engineer, described the efficiency of a Pelton wheel, (as high as 80 percent). But though that seemed the way to go so far as water wheels or turbines for high head installations such as I contemplated, the major problem a small hydroelectric installation faces is getting the current "in phase" with one's utility. The regulatory mechanism, whether mechanical or electronic, is costly and complicated and mitigated against alternating current generating on a small scale. Alternating current literally "alternates" positive and negative poles, sixty times a second, the common frequency used by utilities in America.

To solve this problem, this friend suggested I write his Alma Mater, Rensselaer Polytechnic Institute, to find out what its professors might suggest. This I did, along with letters to the Massachusetts Institute of Technology and other schools.

By now I had made some rough preliminary calculations as to what my brook might provide. One frosty morning in January, when the mercury stood at −15 degrees Fahrenheit, I chopped a hole in the ice at the gate to the dam I had built for fire protection and a swimming hole. Lo and behold four inches of water were flowing through the 42 inch opening, or more than one cubic foot a second even in the dead of winter. Then, I took the altimeter off my car and walked up the road on the brookside, to get a rough idea of the head, or number of feet of drop the brook would provide. The altimeter was graduated in 200 feet invervals. Roughly it seemed that there was something like 250 feet of head available.

I carefully outlined my project to several schools, as per the following letter to Rensselaer's Department of Electrical Engineering written May, 1976. I wrote:

Gentlemen:

May I ask your help? I want to find out about a Pelton wheel, where I may obtain one, the size necessary, etc. I have a beautiful stream coursing through my farm. It has about a 250' drop in approximately the half mile on my property. Though the flow slows down in summer, it runs well at least 10 months of the year, particularly in winter, when it is of the most use. I want to harness it. Presently my electric bills—I am at the end of a Rural Electric Administration line, and the rates are stiff—run $70 a month and more. That does not include heat. Fuel oil is about $800 (sic!) a year also. Thus, a sizeable investment should be justified, if I could generate enough electricity for my needs, or even part of my needs.

One of your graduates, . . . a former parishioner of mine from Hartford, Conn., suggested the Spencer Turbine Co. in Hartford could give me information. I wrote, to learn they manufacture turbines for air only. Mr . . . figured that some-

thing like 28 kW would be needed for both heat, and other purposes. If I used the entire 250' fall, what size pipe, and what size Pelton wheel would I need? If I ran a shorter pipe, say with something like a 100' drop, what diameter would I need there?

Our winters are severe—frequently going down to—30 F. in January. Such a line would have to be insulated—buried somewhat, to prevent freezing, I imagine, as I had a ¾" line freeze, even though running full tilt from the spring, 1600' up the mountain. (This happened when I had a temporary above ground connection.)

Can you direct me to a reference work that would give me the information if it is too much to write in a letter? In the early days, there was a water powered saw mill on this stream. All the streams around here were harnessed in the XIXth century. With improved technology I wonder if it is not practical today?

Presently the house has a 7½ kV transformer supplying it.

Any information you can give me will be greatly appreciated.

Sincerely yours,
J. George Butler

The letter to MIT drew a complete blank. Rensselaer was almost as bad. It said:

Dear Mr. Butler:

In reply to your recent letter, let me tell you that we don't have within our department those people who might be able to help you with your problem. I am, however, passing your letter along to our Mechanical Engineering Department and to the Electric Power Engineering Center.

Best of luck.

Sincerely,
/ . . . . Chairman
Electric Engineering Curriculum

The Mechanical Engineering Department did indeed respond. It suggested that I write the James Leffel Co., Springfield, Ohio, but I already knew of the James Leffel Co. It made a Hoppes Unit, self-contained, for $10,000. This unit with the cost of pipe, building a dam, and powerhouse, made the project completely unrealistic from an economic point of view.

Another friend, a graduate of Norwich University in Vermont, also a good engineering school, suggested I write one of his former professors. I did so, but again, I was disappointed. I received no practical help.

In desperation I wrote General Electric and then Allis Chalmers. I pestered Vermont's Department of Water Resources, its Environmental Commission, and the New England Branch of the Army Corps of Engineers. None could give practical suggestions.

Finally I extended my search world-wide. I wrote to the embassies of China, Sweden, Norway, Germany, Switzerland, Japan, and many others. I had learned from the Bulletin of the Atomic Scientists (February, 1977) of China's intermediate technology, of its 70,000 small hydro installations averaging 42 kW each, turning out about 3,000,000 kWs of power. No reply was forthcoming. I wrote my Senators, asking if they could pry information from the Chinese. They could not.

The Japanese wrote of a very interesting experiment they were conducting: attempting to harness the mechanical energy of the waves. The Germans, the Swiss, and the Norwegians responded. By far the most interesting reply came from Sweden, from the Scientific Attache to its embassy in Washington.

He wrote in June 1976:

Dear Mr. Butler:
. . . Yes, there is a growing interest in Sweden today for the use of small hydro-power units in the 100 kW size range. The idea is to manufacture standardized units in relatively large series and then adapt each unit for a specific site by e.g. using adjustable turbine blades. Preferably should sites which in the past have been used for grinders, sawmills, etc. be used . . . .

Sincerely,
Assistant Scientific Attache

Finally, the Federal Department of Energy announced a small pilot program for feasibility studies of low head hydroelectric development. By this time I was Town Energy Coordinator for Halifax, Vermont. I immediately set about to obtain federal funds to investigate this town project I dreamed about for the North River. The New England Division of the Army Corps of Engineers encouraged me to proceed, giving a very favorable once over lightly review of the North River situation.

Our town was serviced by the Vermont Electric Cooperative with a distribution system in place. Though Halifax comprises 36 square miles, its permanent population is only about 400. Hence, if this project could be built, it would provide enough power for the town, and bring in excellent revenue as well as using a renewable, non-polluting resource. The Co-op liked the idea. The townsfolk like the idea of lower taxes.

To obtain the blessing of the Vermont Electric Co-op, I had to run up to Johnson, Vermont, 180 miles away. En route, I stopped by Waterbury, Vermont where Green Mountain Power Co. was installing a 5 MW wheel and made the friendship of Harry McKay, water wheel erector from Port Colborne, Ontario. Harry told me, in response to my query: "The best hydro engineer in the business is Steve Kleinschmidt, of Pittsfield, Maine. He is not only competent, but a splendid person also. I know you will like him."

Additionally, Harry told me of the English firm he represented, Gilbert, Gilkes, and Gordon, who made small, very efficient turbines. I immediately wrote them, only to learn what I had learned previously: small units were available, but their price, translating pounds into dollars, was prohibitive.

Harry told me that Steve's firm worked on a four day week, beginning at 7 am and quitting at 6 pm to save energy. And 7 am telephone calls were 60 percent cheaper than day rates! So next morning, I was talking with Steve and he was all Harry said he was, and more.

"Yes," he said, "I'll take a look at your town project as soon as I can." To be sure I had the right man, I checked both the State Department of Water Resources, and the Army Corps of Engineers. Did they know Steve Kleinschmidt? And what did they think of him?

Indeed they did, was the reply from both: the most respected hydro man in the business.

Thus began my acquaintance with R. Stevens Kleinschmidt, DSc, Harvard, whose practical concern, imagination, generosity and work, has made my hydroelectric project a reality. After years of frustration, Steve's theoretical know-how, and his desire to test empirically his dreams for an economically feasible, and workable small scale hydroelectric generating plant, far simpler than the complex devices presently on the market, set me on my way.

Shortly after my call, Steve stopped by, while on an engineering trip to southern New Hampshire. After looking over the North River situation, he thought it worth a preliminary feasibility study and agreed to do it.

As I fixed lunch for him (my wife being away at school in Brattleboro) Steve said (in response to my talk about the brook) "I'll tell you how you can harness it." He explained briefly his theories that small scale hydro development could be made very practical and economically attractive.

In short order, the Town had Steve's preliminary findings on the North River. It was worth harnessing. So I set out to draw up a grant application from the Department of Energy for the Town.

We were turned down. No reason was given.

I demanded under the Freedom of Information Act to know why.

The answer finally came. The Town project exceeded the parameters of the grant program for low head hydro. The limit for this application was 20 meters, or about 66 feet, the arbitrary limits DOE had set for low head hydro. And Halifax had 100′ of head. It was quite simple: the North River sites, with their beautiful natural falls, which would only require a six foot dam to harness 100′ of head, exceeded the parameters set by DOE.

Maddened and frustrated at such colossal stupidity by bungling bureaucrats I called a contact at DOE. This subaltern, a likeable chap, said, when told of our turndown: "Oh, we didn't think of that when we wrote the regulations for this program."

9

Sarcastically, I wrote our Congressional delegation—all three of them—"Halifax was turned down because it had too much head. Somebody in Washington has far too little head!"

Maybe I did some good. Finally a year and more later, this inane limit on "head" was deleted from the regulations. And now, several years later, after my own hydro on the farm is completed, we reapplied for the feasibility funds for the Town, and finally obtained a 90-10 percent feasibility loan from DOE. That is, the Department puts up $45,000 for feasibility, with the town putting up $5,000. If the project turns out to be a good one, the town capitalizes the cost of the feasibility study. If the project turns out to be no good, the loan is forgiven. As this is being written, engineering studies are finally under way, and if the projections hold, and no further snags arise, the Town may finally re-use this renewable energy resource. After all, we are supposed to be in an energy emergency.

This is ahead of the story. I mention it, because of the part my own hydro-electric project on my brook played. The Chinese say, "One picture is worth a thousand words." It was the picture of my small 10 kW project which stirred the imagination of the townsfolk and enabled them to see the value of the municipal project I had talked about for so long.

Chapter 2

Reasons for Thinking Small

America is a nation of bigness: vast distances, large factories, and giant power stations. Its slogan seemingly is: bigger is better. Why then, realizing the "economies of scale," should one bother to think small?

The answer is simple and straightforward. In the 100 years of the electric age, most large hydroelectric sites have been developed. While the late David E. Lilienthal did argue eloquently for the development of smaller sized projects, no one until now has come up with an inexpensive and successful way to harness the myriad small sites which are to be found wherever there is hill country. This technology, conceived by Dr. Kleinschmidt, and put to the empirical test, has demonstrated that it is relatively simple and economical to harness small streams. Up to now they have been by-passed due to the difficulties in making such current generated by these small installations synchronous with one's utility (60 Hz).

THE DEVELOPMENT OF HYDROPOWER IN NEW ENGLAND

In 1881, Thomas A. Edison started building the first central generating station in the world. Completed in 1882, the old direct current Pearl St. Station in New York City was the marvel of the age. Four years later, an enterprising group

11

of men in Vermont turned on the first hydroelectric station in that state. Familiar with water wheels, or turbines, they tapped a 10 inch water main to supply electricity for street lights in Montpelier.

New England was rich in water power. One of the first large (for that day) hydroelectric installations in Vermont was the hydro station built just south of Brattleboro, in Vernon. Built between 1907 and 1909, this project is of more than historical interest (see Fig. 2-1). In the days when it was built, and indeed for many decades thereafter, little consideration was given to environmental concerns. Modern earth moving equipment was not yet invented. High pressure, hydraulic hoses were used to cut away the earth, causing untold pollution downstream. But the builders of this concrete dam, 600 feet long, thirty feet high, built well. And the turbines, installed in 1909 are still churning out electricity, as they have now for 72 years. They bear eloquent testimony to the fact that a hydroelectric plant, properly maintained can last practically forever.

To increase the height (or head) three and four inch pipes on top of the concrete support 8 feet of flash boards. Each

Fig. 2-1. This is the Vernon hydroelectric station, built in 1909. Note at extreme left, partially shaded by overhanging trees the "new" section of the station, built in 1919 (courtesy of New England Power Company).

Fig. 2-2. This transformer standing on the floor of the hydroelectric station is a spare, waiting since 1909, when the station was built, to be put into service. Today, 72 years later, it still stands, in its original crate, waiting for use.

spring, when river flow exceeds the capacity of the flood gates and all ten turbines running full tilt, the 3 inch pipes go first, then the 4 inch, and when the flood subsides, the dam crew has the rather simple job of putting new pipes in the holes, and replacing the planks that have washed downstream.

As one goes through the station, he sees a new, yet old, uncrated "spare" transformer, sitting alongside those in service (see Fig. 2-2). Bill Wocjik explained to me: "This is the spare transformer we have had ready to use since the plant was built, in case one of the others failed. But they built so much excess capacity in them in those days, that it is still sitting there, waiting to be put on line—since 1909!"

Bill was careful to tell me that the plant was "modernized" in 1919 with the addition of two more generating units. These units turn at a speed of but 75 rpm, whereas the "old" units turn at 133.3 rpm (see Figs. 2-3 and 2-4). Each generator has a vertical shaft extending below it to three turbines, mounted one below the other. Thus the water, falling from the top, continues to spin the rotor of the generator and has done so, with regular maintenance for these many years.

The drainage basin of the Connecticut River at Vernon is 6,266 square miles. While this provides adequate flow to run

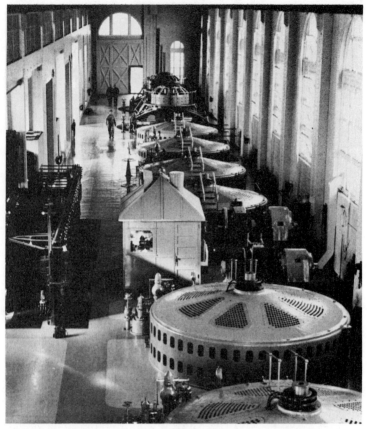

Fig. 2-3. View of Turbine Hall of the Vernon Station on the Connecticut River, a few miles below Brattleboro, Vermont. The "new" turbines, installed in 1919 are the two at the end of the hall, nearest the door, or shore side at the end of the building (courtesy of New England Power Company).

all ten generators during the spring runoff, and in other wet parts of the year, during summer droughts, only two or three generating units are run steadily. In case of peak demand however, all ten can be run at once, generating 28 megawatts, and drawing down the pond behind the dam only 10 inches in eight hours.

The Vernon Dam is the most southerly of six operated by New England Power on the Connecticut River. Beginning at the Connecticut Lakes on the Canadian border, water is used as determined by electric demand. For instance, the Bellows

Falls dam, 25 miles upstream from Vernon, even with less drainage area than Vernon, has a capacity of 45 MW, because it has a head of 60 feet. Water released by this dam, takes eight hours to reach Vernon, where of course, it is again reused to generate power.

Vernon's machinery is so old, spare parts are no longer obtainable. Hence New England Power must maintain its own machine shop to make whatever is needed. Trash: flotsam and jetsam, is removed from the trash racks by the good old fashioned wheelbarrow, perhaps antiquated to modern eyes, but certainly foolproof. Wintertime vagaries have taught the Power Company how to cope with "Old Man River." One of the tricks of the trade is to bubble up compressed air from the bottom of the dam, thus bringing relatively warm water up from the bottom and preventing ice from forming on flood gates and flash boards.

Like all other sections of the country, the age of canal transportation saw small dams, locks, and canals around dangerous rapids. By 1849, the first power dam had been built at Holyoke, Massachusetts. Other dams followed. With the age of hydroelectricity, the upper reaches of the river were

Fig. 2-4. This Francis turbine sits alongside the uncrated "spare" transformer in turbine hall, of the Vernon hydroelectric station. It was originally installed at the Vernon station in 1909 and taken out of service in the early 1940s. Refurbished by the maintenance staff at Vernon, this wheel is waiting to be put back into use, if needed.

effectively blocked to anadromous fish. The Atlantic salmon and Connecticut River shad disappeared.

This past year, a 10½ million dollar fishway, or ladder was completed at Vernon, costing more than twice the original cost of the powerhouse and dam (see Figs. 2-5 through 2-8). Now, these valuable fish are once again making their way up river to spawn in such areas as the White River. Interestingly, such anadromous fish swim up fish ladders only during daylight hours. At night, only 64 cfs are discharged over the fishway, compared to 200 cfs during daylight hours. Slack water is provided in each pool which rises 6 inches higher than the previous, to allow the fish to rest.

South of Vernon, Northeast Utilities has several dams from Turners Falls and Holyoke, Massachusetts to Windsor Locks and Enfield, Connecticut.

A decade ago Northeast Utilities built its Northfield Mountain pumped storage facility. Using the Connecticut River, impounded by the Turners Falls dam into a 20 mile lake as a reservoir Northeast Utilities built an enormous upper reservoir atop Northfield Mountain. At night, when demand for electricity is generally low, and there is more than enough electricity available, the power company uses that surplus power to pump water from the river, or lower reservoir to the top of the mountain, so that it can be used in times of peak demand (see Fig. 2-9).

Fig. 2-5. Vernon hydroelectric station and dam as it looks now. This photo shows the recently constructed fish ladder in the foreground. The "new" part of the powerhouse, built in 1919, is at the left, next to the fishway.

Fig. 2-6. The fish ladder at the Vernon station was completed in 1981 so that Atlantic Salmon could again run upriver to spawn. At present, the fishway at Bellows falls is not quite complete, so salmon and other anadromous fish are transported by tanker truck from Vernon above Bellows Falls, 25 miles upriver where they are released so they can reach the White River and other tributaries of the Connecticut. Each "step" has a six inch rise, and is designed so that fish may rest in slack water at each step. The total cost of the fish ladder at Vernon was over $10 million.

In 1972, when Northfield Mountain came on line, it was the largest pumped storage facility in the world. To date, such pumped storage facilities are the only way large amounts of energy can be stored. By pumping water up to the top of the

Fig. 2-7. The upper segment of the fishway leads to the upper level of the river above the dam. Because of the necessity for access to the plant, the top part is covered by a steel grating.

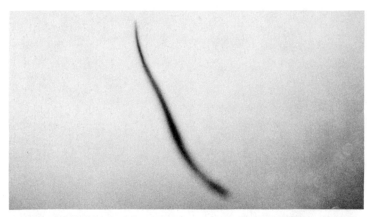

Fig. 2-8. This photo was taken through the observation window where visitors may view the fish swimming upstream. Here an eel is making its way from the bottom to the top of the dam.

mountain, from 60 to 75 percent of the energy can be recovered when needed, by having that same water turn generators on the way down (see Fig. 2-10).

In this facility, specially made hybrid pumps were designed to serve both as pumps to push the water up, and as turbines that the water would turn on the way down. The reservoir atop the mountain covers 320 acres, 1000 feet and more above sea level. It can store 15,230 acre feet, or 660 million cubic feet of water, and can generate 1000 MWs for as long as ten hours, if necessary. In practice the plant is not run for more than six or seven hours at a time.

When the plant starts generating electricity, the water rushes down a shaft, 31 feet in diameter, falling 785 feet to the powerhouse, located 2500 feet inside the mountain. The powerhouse itself is 385 feet long, and is taller than a ten story building. The noise of water rushing through 1100 feet of penstock sounds like a thousand express trains were rushing at you at once. (see Figs. 2-11 through 2-13).

THE DEVELOPMENT OF HYDROPOWER IN THE REST OF THE NATION

Though the Connecticut River was well harnessed, and tributaries such as the Deerfield, a small stream rising in

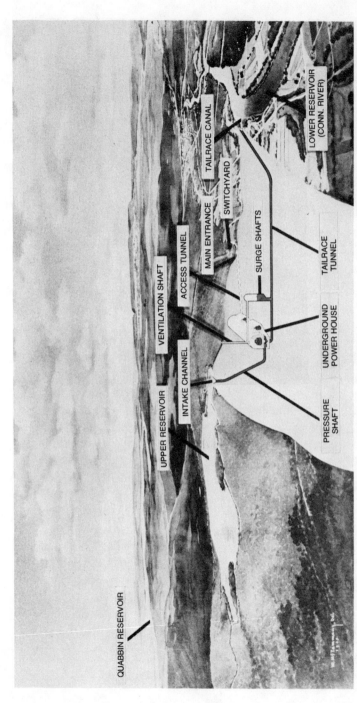

QUABBIN RESERVOIR

UPPER RESERVOIR

VENTILATION SHAFT

INTAKE CHANNEL

ACCESS TUNNEL

MAIN ENTRANCE

SWITCHYARD

TAILRACE CANAL

SURGE SHAFTS

PRESSURE SHAFT

UNDERGROUND POWER HOUSE

TAILRACE TUNNEL

LOWER RESERVOIR (CONN. RIVER)

Fig. 2-9. When it was built in 1972, the Northfield Pumped Storage plant was the largest such facility in the world (courtesy of Northeast Utilities).

19

Fig. 2-10. Here is an aerial view of the Northfield Reservoir on top of Northfield Mountain. It has a capacity of 660 million cubic feet of water (courtesy of Northeast Utilities).

Fig. 2-11. The entrance of the tunnel through the mountain to the powerhouse which is 2500 feet inside the mountain (courtesy of Northeast Utilities).

21

Fig. 2-12. The powerhouse of the Northfield Mountain Pumped Storage station is located 2500 feet inside the mountain (courtesy of Northeast Utilities).

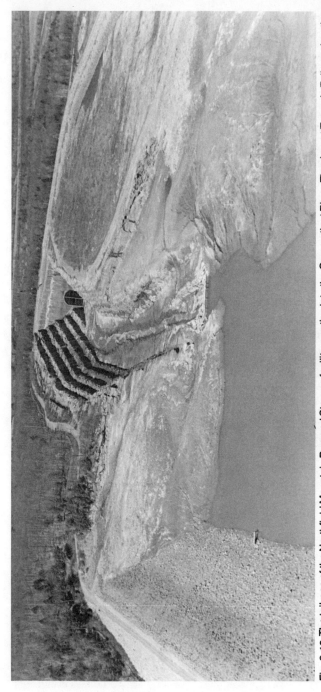

Fig. 2-13. The tailrace of the Northfield Mountain Pumped Storage facility empties into the Connecticut River. The dam at Turner's Falls, makes the Connecticut a navigable lake 20 miles long at this point. During the summer Northeast Utilities runs excursions on the lake for visitors. Picnic facilities are also available for nature lovers atop the mountain overlooking the lake and tours are arranged through the powerhouse (courtesy of Northeast Utilities).

23

Southwestern Vermont and joining the Connecticut at historic Deerfield, Massachusetts had eight power dams in less than 100 miles, the mighty streams of the American West were not far behind in being utilized.

As early as 1885, the Pacific Gas and Electric Co., along with state and federal help harnessed the Willamette River, a tributary of the Columbia. In 1910, Portland (Oregon) General Electric Company was also building dams on the Willamette, followed by a dam on the Sandy River in 1912. As shown in Table 2-1, the great push for hydroelectric dams did not come until the 1930s.

The Pacific Northwest Regional Commission, commenting on the lack of environmental concern by these dam builders, said: "The U.S. Bureau of Reclamation completed Grand Coulee Dam in 1941. Built without fish ladders, it blocked salmon and steelhead from more than 1,100 miles of tributary spawning and rearing habitat in the upper Columbia Basin." Similarly: "The failure of fish passage facilities at Idaho Power Company's Brownlee Dam on the middle Snake River in the early 1960s terminated all fish passage to and from the upper Snake River Basin." As a result of such short sightedness, this report continues: "Water project developers have made capital expenditures of more than $269 million for salmon and steelhead passage and compensation facilities in the Columbia Basin."

Table 2-1. Mainstream Columbia and Snake River Dams
(courtesy of Pacific Northwest Regional Commission).

Columbia River	Year of Initial Service	Snake River	Year of Initial Service
Rock Island	1933	Swan Falls	1910
Bonneville	1938	Lower Salmon Falls	1910
Grand Coulee	1941	Bliss	1949
McNary	1935	C.J.Strike	1952
Chief Joseph	1955	Brownlee	1958
The Dalles	1957	Oxbow	1961
Priest Rapids	1959	Ice Harbor	1961
Rocky Reach	1961	Hells Canyon	1967
Wanapum	1963	Lower Monumental	1969
Wells	1967	Little Goose	1970
John Day	1968	Lower Granite	1975

Fig. 2-14. The Hoover Dam on the Colorado River, completed in 1936 is still one of the largest hydroelectric dams in the world (courtesy of Water and Power Resources Service).

During this same period of the 1930s, the great Hoover Dam on the Colorado River was built. Completed in 1936, this dam is still one of the largest dams in the world. It is 726 feet high, 1,244 feet long, and backs up the waters forming Lake Mead for 115 miles. Used for flood control and irrigation purposes for more than one million acres, the Hoover Dam, has a rated hydroelectric capacity of 1,344,800 kilowatts (see Figs. 2-14 and 2-15).

THE ARMY CORPS OF ENGINEERS

The Army Corps of Engineers produces more hydroelectricity than any other agency in America. How the Army Engineers came into this role is interesting. In 1824, Congress gave the Engineers the responsibility of keeping the Ohio and Mississippi Rivers open for navigation by clearing snags and sandbars for the growing steamboat traffic. Today, it is still at it, not only on these rivers, but on others as well. From this initial responsibility for rivers and harbor navigation, the Army Engineers' responsibility grew to include hydroelectric power.

In 1909, the Federal government acquired its first hydroelectric facility, a dam on the St. Mary's River in Michigan. The principal purpose of this dam was to provide deeper water for navigational purposes. Also, a small hydroelectric station was built.

Alert members of Congress, seeing the advantages of this new technology and its tremendous importance to the industrial growth of the nation, pushed legislation giving the Corps jurisdiction to study all potential hydroelectric sites. In 1916, the first hydro installation attempted by the Army Engineers was the addition of another turbine and generator at the St. Mary's plant. Then, during World War I, the Engineers began building the Wilson Dam, and locks at Muscle Shoals in Alabama, which became the forerunner of the Tennessee Valley Authority. The first great project in the West undertaken by the Army Engineers was the Bonneville Dam on the Columbia River, completed in 1938. Since World War II the Corps has greatly expanded its role in hydroelectric development. All over the nation, except in New England, Army Engineers' dams have been dual purpose, or triple purpose projects: flood control and irrigation, as well as hydroelectric. Only in New England have all its dams been single purpose structures: flood control. When I asked an official of the Corps why this was so he said: "Because your State Legislature wouldn't let us."

Perhaps this is but part of the story. New England Rivers, not already harnessed, by private power companies, are generally small and have relatively low capacity factors. A capacity factor is the percentage of the time a power station is calculated to be able to operate. For instance, the Vermont Electric Cooperative is now retrofitting the North Hartland Vermont flood control dam, built in the early 1960s by the Engineers, on the Ottauquechee, a small stream flowing into the Connecticut just below White River Junction. This facility

Fig. 2-15. The Hoover Dam's powerhouse is directly below the dam, as shown in this photo (courtesy of Bureau of Reclamation U.S. Dept. of the Interior).

will have a capacity factor of just over 40 percent. Its 12 million kilowatt hours will form a valuable addition to the Cooperative's grid in providing peaking power, for periods of high demand.

THE TENNESSEE VALLEY AUTHORITY

No discussion of the development of hydropower in the nation would be complete, however, without mention of the Tennessee Valley Authority. Finally signed into law in 1933 by President Franklin D. Roosevelt, after having twice been vetoed by Presidents Coolidge and Hoover, the Tennessee Valley Authority not only opened up the Tennessee River to navigation for 600 miles, it also rejuvenated the life of a seven state region, as well as generating enormous amounts of hydroelectricity. First utilizing the Wilson Dam at Muscle Shoals, other dams quickly followed. Special mention should be made of the Norris Dam, named after Senator George W. Norris of Nebraska, the real father of the TVA, whose indomitable spirit finally led to its creation. By 1960, the TVA had a capacity in excess of 3 million kilowatts of hydropower. The TVA however, mirrors what has happened to big hydro sites. The nation is running out of them. Though such projects as the Tellico Dam are being built, big hydro becomes increasingly expensive and the sites for additional development are simply not available in "the lower 48". By early 1970s, the TVA was producing about 20 percent of its 100 billion kilowatt hours output by hydropower.

ARE WE OUT OF HYDROPOWER?

From these sketches of representative rivers in the East, the Northwest, and the South, one might be led to conclude that there isn't much future for hydropower in the United States. In 1975, a Massachusetts Energy Policy Office Study had this to say about hydroelectric power. "Hydroelectric power and natural gas are both important sources in other parts of the country, but both are unavailable for further New England large-scale generation: there are not any more major sites suitable for hydroelectric power and natural gas is already in critically short supply."

In 1977 a Connecticut Public Utilities Control Authority study on the Economic Aspects of Nuclear Electric Generation said: "The pattern of hydropower generation of electricity illustrated in exhibit 7 (an exhibit by Dr. Ralph Lapp, a leading nuclear advocate) shows that over much of the first half of the century hydropower production was about one third of the total U.S. annual production. However by 1974 the hydropower contribution had decreased to some 16% of the total although actual output had continued to increase. The projections in Exhibit 8 (again Dr. Lapp) indicate that while hydropower generation is expected to increase in the future, the contribution from this source will amount to only about 6% of the total production in the year 2000."

These two conclusions, one from Massachusetts, the other from Connecticut are erroneous because they consider only big hydro projects. David Lilienthal's small or intermediate projects, from 5,000 kilowatts up, could treble the present 16% hydro if we used the 50,000 existing dams 25 feet and more in height. My own belief is: if America thinks small, and sees that "Small Is Beautiful," the potential for hydroelectricity is practically unlimited.

Chapter 3

Answering Questions

"How much power can I get from this stream?" This is always the first question one hears about hydroelectricity. Before it can be answered, one must first measure the flow, and measure the head. Once this is done, the question can then be answered. Before one embarks on such a project, he must also ask himself: "How much power do I need?" Before one goes ahead building his dream, he must ask further: "What are the environmental constraints confronting me, imposed by both state and federal law?

Of these, the amount of energy needed is the easiest question to answer. If you are already connected to a utility, figure from your monthly bills your average power consumption. If the stream won't provide quite that much, then you have some serious cost questions before you. Because the business of benefits to be received compared with cost is so complicated I have left a detailed consideration of this question until later in this book.

Should one not be connected to a utility at present, he will have to go a somewhat different road than I did, but one that is very feasible. Without a utility with which to interconnect, one's needs in relation to the output of his plant become doubly important. If one's energy needs are greater than the possible supply, the answer, is no. To help in ascertaining the amount of electricity one might need see Table 3-1 from Vermont Electric Cooperative's "Co-op Life". To the total one thinks he needs, one should add about 50 kWhs just for lights. Three, 100 watt bulbs, burning on average 5 hours a day, would burn just about 45 k Wh in a month.

In general terms, however, one can consider any brook worth harnessing if it has the potential of supplying even 2 kilowatts. Even this small amount of power mounts up over a month to be 1440 kilowatt hours. Average electric bills are usually not more than 1000 kWh a month.

Again in general terms, any stream which presents the opportunity of harnessing a fall of 100 feet and has a flow of half a cubic foot a second will do the trick. Such conditions should give in the neighborhood of 2 kilowatts or more. Bear in mind that flow and head are reciprocal numbers. Double the flow, and with but half the head, one obtains the same amount of power, and vice versa. Some streams with larger flow are successfully harnessed with heads of but 15 to 20 feet.

BUILDING THE WEIR

The first step in analyzing one's prospective site is: determination of the flow. A short cut method is to find an "ideal" spot, where the banks of the stream are parallel, where there are no rocks or other obstructions to the free flow of the water, and where the depth is quite uniform. Since an ideal is by nature something which cannot be attained, don't be disappointed if your stream does not present you with these conditions. A helpful booklet, published under contract by the National Center for Appropriate Technology, for the U.S. Department of Energy, Idaho Operations Office, Idaho Falls, Idaho, Micro-Hydro Power contains the equations necessary to calculate flow from width, depth, and the time it takes a float to travel a predetermined distance, say 30 or 40 feet.

The most accurate method of determining volume is to build a *weir*. A weir is a temporary dam. Engineers use it to find the rate of flow in cubic feet per second (cfs), or cubic feet per minute (cfm).

31

Table 3-1. Cost of Various Electrical Appliances
(courtesy of Vermont Electric Cooperative, Inc., Johnson, Vt.).

Food Preservation	Average Wattage	Estimated kWh Consumed Annually	Annual Cost At 7¢ per KWh	Average Monthly Cost	
Freezer, 15 cu. ft.	341	1,195	$83.65	$6.97	
Freezer, 15 cu. ft., frostless	440	1,761	123.27	10.27	
Refrigerator, 12 cu. ft.	241	728	50.96	4.24	
Refrigerator, 12 cu. ft., frostless	321	1,217	85.19	7.09	
Refrigerator-Freezer, 14 cu. ft.	326	1,137	79.59	6.63	
Refrigerator-Freezer, 14 cu. ft., frostless	615	1,829	128.03	10.66	
Food Preparation					
Blender	386	15	$1.05	$0.08	
Boiler	1,436	100	7.00	0.59	
Carving knife	92	8	0.56	0.04	
Coffeemaker	894	106	7.42	0.61	
Deepfryer	1,488	83	5.81	0.48	
Dishwasher	1,201	363	25.41	2.11	
Egg Cooker	576	14	0.91	0.07	
Frying Pan	1,196	186	13.01	1.00	**Watch These!**
Hot Plate	1,257	90	6.30	0.52	Tank or block heaters
Mixer (hand)	127	13	0.91	0.07	
Microwave Oven	1,500	300	21.00	1.75	
Self-cleaning Oven	4,800	1,146	80.22	6.69	
Range	8,200	1,175	82.25	6.85	
Roaster	1,333	205	14.35	1.19	
Sandwich Grill	1,161	33	2.21	0.19	
Toaster	1,146	39	2.73	0.23	Portable heaters,
Trash Compactor	400	60	4.20	0.35	
Waffle Iron	1,116	22	1.54	0.12	
Waste Disposer	445	30	2.10	0.18	

Tank or block heaters They are made for various heating capacities, from 500 to 2,000 watts. Although equipped with thermostats, the heater can be expensive to operate during prolonged cold weather. A kilowatt heater (1,000 watts) will cost at least 50 cents over a ten hour period, and, if plugged in each night, $15.00 by month's end.

Portable heaters, No magic here! The quartz heater is just like any other portable heater. Most of them have two 750 watt elements. When turned on, they therefore use 1500 watts, or one and a half kilowatts, just like most portables. Count on them costing 10½ cents an hour to operate since we generally use portable heaters during very cold weather in rooms too large to heat to the highest thermostat setting—and we usually have them turned on full in order to get all the heat possible from them!

Comfort Conditioning			
Air Cleaner	50	216	$15.12	$1.26
Bed Covering	177	200	14.00	1.16
Dehumidifier	257	377	26.39	2.39
Fan (attic)	370	291	20.37	1.70
Fan (circulating)	88	43	3.01	0.25
Fan (rollaway)	171	138	9.66	0.81
Fan (window)	200	170	11.90	0.99
Heating pad	65	10	0.70	0.05
Humidifier	177	163	11.41	0.95
Health and Beauty			
Germicidal Lamp	20	141	9.87	0.82
Hairdryer	381	14	0.98	0.08
Heat Lamp (infra-red)	250	13	0.91	0.07
Shaver	14	1.8	0.12	0.01
Sunlamp	279	16	1.12	0.09
Toothbrush	7	0.5	0.03	
Vibrator	40	2	0.14	
Laundry			
Clothes Dryer	4,856	1,000	70.00	$5.83
Iron (hand)	1,008	144	10.08	0.84
Washing Machine	512	103	7.21	0.60
Water Heater	2,475	4,219	295.33	24.61
Water Heater (quick recovery)	4,474	4,811	336.77	28.06
Home Entertainment			
Radio	71	86	6.02	0.50
Radio-Record Player	109	109	7.63	0.64
TV B-W Tube	160	350	24.50	2.04
TV B-W Solid State	55	120	8.40	0.70
TV Color Tube	300	660	46.20	3.85
TV color Solid State	200	440	30.80	2.57
Housewares			
Clock	2	17	1.19	0.10
Floor Polisher	305	15	1.05	0.08
Sewing Machine	75	11	0.77	0.06
Vacuum Cleaner	630	47	3.29	0.28

Note: These estimates are based on an average cost of seven cents per kilowatt hour, and may vary dramatically depending on how many kilowatt hours you use per month.

Someone said building a weir is easier said than done. If one has any of the boy left in him, it can still be play. Who in his youth, or adolescence has not played in a stream, rolling stones to make a crossing, and attempting to dam the flow enough to increase the depth of a wading pool? If one is adept with Tom Sawyer's technique, building a weir can be just as much fun as one's childhood games, and far more useful.

Inveigling two friends to share my "fun", we built a weir in one morning. The first task was to clear as many rocks as we could, so that the bottom edge of the 2 × 8 planks would rest on the stream bottom. We also wanted them as nearly level as we could get them, but Vermont's streams are notoriously rocky. Driving stakes into the stream bed was quite impossible in many places. Hence we had to hold the planks in place by chocking them with large rocks. From the first course so positioned, we nailed a second course of 2 × 8 planks. This brought us just above the normal stream level, so we were then ready for the 6 foot gate through which the stream would flow, when we built the weir up on either side of it. See Figs. 3-1 and 3-2.

If feasible, it is wise to put the gate so as to be accessible for measuring the flow on the side of the stream. Two more courses of 2 × 8 planks gave us the start of a very respectable weir. I say start, because then came the difficult task of

Fig. 3-1. Gary and Dan MacArthur (left to right) at the spillway of the newly erected weir. Note rocks for bracing on the back side.

Fig. 3-2. Here I am measuring the flow over weir gate, after as many leaks as possible were stopped.

making the weir water tight. We used silt, rocks, sand, mud, soft coal clinkers, rags, sawdust, sod from the banks, anything we could lay our hands on to try to stop the flow of water under the planks. Finally we achieved a measure of success. I am partial to sawdust to stop leaks between boards because as soon as it is carried into a crack it swells and the leak is stopped.

In order to measure the flow accurately, many authorities advise driving a stake 10 feet upstream from the middle of the weir gate, using a carpenter's level and a straight piece of lumber to mark on the stake the point exactly level with the top of the weir. From then on up, gradations can be marked so that readings of depth may be taken by a glance. See Table 3-2. Perhaps a simpler method and one that is nearly as accurate is to measure the water going over the gate itself. True, the water picks up speed as it flows over the gate, but by placing one's rule perpendicular, on top of the gate, broadside to the flow, one can read the flow as measured on the upstream side in inches. The resistance of the water against the rule will just about compensate for the added velocity, and hence, lower depth of the water as it flows over the edge of the gate.

As one studies stream flow, I should mention a popular misconception about small hydro. Many people remember the mill ponds of long ago. They are not important, in terms of

Table 3-2. A Weir Table is Used to Determine Cubic Feet
Per Minute from the Depth of Water at a Stake. For Cubic Feet Per Second,
Divide by 60 (courtesy of The National Center for Appropriate Technology).

Depth on Stake (in inches)	c.f.m. per inch of Notch Width	Depth on Stake (in Inches)	c.f.m. per Inch of Notch Width
1	0.40	12.5	17.78
1.25	0.55	12.75	18.32
1.5	0.74		
1.75	0.93	13	18.87
		13.25	19.42
2	1.14	13.5	19.97
2.25	1.36	13.75	20.52
2.5	1.59		
2.75	1.83	14	21.09
		14,25	21.65
3	2.09	14.5	22.22
3.25	2.36	14.75	22.70
3.5	2.63		
3.75	2.92	15	23.38
		15.25	23.97
4	3.22	15.5	24.56
4.25	3.52	15.75	25.16
4.5	3.83		
4.75	4.16	16	25.76
		16.25	26.36
5	4.50	16.5	26.97
5.25	4.84	16.75	27.58
5.5	5.18		
5.75	5.54	17	28.20
		17.25	28.82
6	5.90	17.5	29.45
6.25	6.28	17.75	30.08
6.5	6.65		
6.75	7.05	18	30.70
		18.25	31.34
7	7.44	18.5	31.98
7.25	7.84	18.75	32.63
7.5	8.25		
7.75	8.66	19	33.29
		19.25	33.94
8	9.10	19.5	34.60
8.25	9.52	19.75	35.27
8.5	9.96		
8.75	10.40	20	35.94
		20.25	36.60
9	10.86	20.5	37.28
9.25	11.31	20.75	37.96
9.5	11.77		
9.75	12.23	21	38.65
		21.25	39.34
10	12.71	21.5	40.04
10.25	13.19	21.75	40.73
10.5	13.67		
10.75	14.16	22	41.43
		22.25	42.13
11	14.67	22.5	42.84
11.25	15.18	22.75	43.56
11.5	15.67		
11.75	16.20	23	44.28
		23.25	45.00
12	16.73	23.5	45.71
12.25	17.26	23.75	46.43
		24	47.18

storing up water to run a small hydro. The stream must have enough flow to enable one to run constantly, not intermittently. The purpose of the dam is not primarily to store water, to be drained down, as the old grist mill or saw mill did. Rather, it is to provide a means to take the water out of the stream, via the penstock. Should one have enough pondage to run for hours, it still would not be enough unless the flow of the stream is adequate to equal the amount of water necessary to run the turbine.

It is essential that one measures stream flow when it is low. Small streams run dry quite frequently in summer. This is not necessarily a fatal handicap, but it does mean, during the dry summer months, one must let the minimum flow the stream has, remain in it, to protect its aquatic life, rather than diverting every last drop to his penstock. Conservation agencies demand this: it is simple common sense that one do it.

One dry summer day I measured the flow in my brook. It's flow was down to a trickle (one gallon a second) certainly not enough for any power and not enough to be diverted into a penstock. I noticed that in stretches, the brook seemed to be running dry, only to reappear several hundred feet downstream in deep pools, where fish had learned to congregate and protect themselves in periods of drought. Many a watercourse does this, going underground where the soil is gravel and sand.

It is simply impossible to try to build a dam high enough to store enough water to carry one through dry spells, hoping thereby to be able to generate power continuously. A small dam, 5 or 6 feet high, is far less costly to build, and far less costly to the environment. It causes no flooding of valuable land or down stream disaster in the event of a dam break, and in the end, enables one to run just as long is if he had large pondage to draw upon. The gristmills and sawmills of yore needed pondage to run for a few hours in many cases, but their water wheels were far less efficient than modern turbines. Most such sites used only a fraction of the head available with today's technology. Bear in mind: the greater the head, the less volume of water for the same amount of power.

One solution to the problem of low water, which is particularly true for small streams everywhere is: use a smaller pump or turbine. A neighbor of mine has two wheels: one turning out 10 kW, the other 5 kW, so that in summer, he can generally run the small one, even with low flow. In the fall, he runs both wheels, turning out 15 kW. This same idea is valid for pumps used as turbines. My present pump, using 1 cubic foot a second, or 7.48 gallons, is too large for much of summer's low flow. A pump, using half a cubic foot a second would run much of the time and would provide more than adequate power for demands during the summer.

MEASURING THE HEAD

After determining the flow of a stream the next step in preparing to harness it is: to measure the head. The only way to obtain an exact measurement is to use a transit. A friend of mine is a surveyor. With his expertise, we ran a level on the river. We knew from our weir that we had plenty of water and the rapids gave me the illusion of a good head. But the transit was objective: we had only 20 feet of fall in 1000 feet. That spelled doom for any idea of using the river for my installation. While low heads may be harnessed in some locations, the topography here precluded it. Large diameter pipe is simply prohibitively expensive. Shelf rock and ledge from the overhanging cliff prevented any thought of digging a canal. The type turbine required for such a low head, would cost too much.

I could use the brook. It was not nearly as large, but it had a big head. My altimeter told me there was something like 250 feet or more of head. With that kind of fall, far less volume would be needed.

The next spring, when it was possible to resume work in earnest, my friend Steve and his son David came by with their surveyor's gear, to check my estimate. As usual, I was a bit too optimistic. There wasn't 250 feet of head. There was only 225 feet available but this would suffice for the kind of installation Steve had in mind. Should anyone desire to harness a head 10 to 20 feet, or even up to fifty feet, the DOE sponsored book: Micro-Hydro Power indicates a cross flow turbine may be suitable. Table 3-3 shows how to calculate probable output of power from two known values: head and flow.

Though 6 inch pvc (polyvinyl chloride) pipe is expensive, it is essential that one obtain a good grade of pipe, capable of withstanding the pressures and stresses to which it will be subjected. From experience in dealing with my spring 1600 feet up the mountain I know this is so. When I developed a beautiful spring so that I would have enough pressure to run

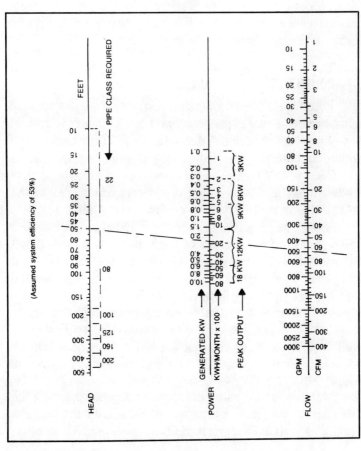

Table 3-3. Nomograph to Determine Typical Output Power from a Micro-Hydro System (courtesy of The National Center for Appropriate Technology).

such new fangled gadgets as a dishwasher and clothes washer, I found I had too much pressure for the 80 pound test pipe I installed. Every year I was patrolling the line, digging it up to repair leaks. The problem was simply that the pressure was over 80 pounds, and the pipe would break periodically. Finally, I had to put in a heavier pipe for the last 800 feet. Since then, I have had no trouble.

In long pipe installations such as mine, friction loss may be a significant factor. Pvc pipe is very smooth and friction is at a minimum. Each joint can "give" a couple of degrees and in summer, when the pipe is warm, it can be bent a few degrees in every twenty foot section. One may be tempted to use old cast iron well casing which is often available from junk yards. This is poor economy since rust makes such pipe very rough, and raises the friction coefficient to unacceptable levels. Table 3-4 shows friction loss in pvc pipe.

ENVIRONMENTAL CONSTRAINTS

Before beginning the actual construction of a project, one must ascertain state environmental laws governing hydropower projects. With small dams, flooding of farm land is not a factor, but diverting flow from a stream bed to a penstock and its effect on aquatic life is very much a consideration. Vermont has some of the strictest environmental laws in the nation, due in part to its rich environmental heritage.

George Perkins Marsh, born in Woodstock, Vermont in 1801, was the fountainhead of the conservation movement. He was a many faceted genius. Graduating first in his class at Dartmouth College in 1820 at the age of 19, he read law and then began its practice in Burlington. By the age of 30 he was fluent in 20 languages. After serving in the Legislature, he went to Congress. He served as Ambassador to Turkey as well as various other countries. Finally, President Lincoln named him Ambassador to Italy where he served for over 20 years.

Marsh was interested in art and architecture, giving the final design to the Washington Monument in the nation's capital, as well as designing the State House in Montpelier.

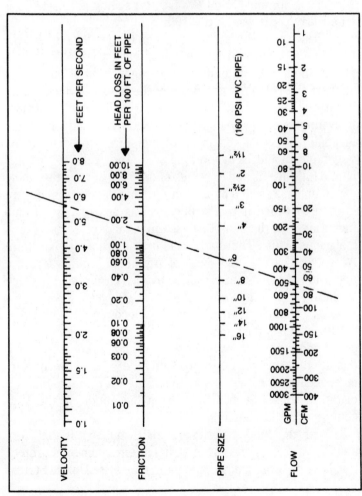

Table 3-4. Nomograph to Determine Losses Due to Friction in Pvc Pipe. (Courtesy: National Center for Appropriate Technology.)

Noted for belles lettres, Marsh wrote his classic, *Man and Nature* which he published in 1864. It was reprinted in the 1930s. In it, 100 years before Rachel Carson talked about the Chain of life in *Silent Spring,* Marsh pointed to the same thing in his writings. Using his tremendous linguistic ability, he saw the tragic damage and erosion caused by man's misuse of the environment. He contrasted the Alps, the Apennines, and the Pyrenees to his beloved Green Mountains of Vermont. He saw the deserts of Africa and decried the rape of the American continent whose riches were thought to be inexhaustable. Marsh's aphorism: "Sight is a faculty: seeing is an art," is as true today, as it was in the 19th century.

He wrote: "The earth was given to men for our use, not for consumption, still less for profligate waste." With passionate pen he continued: "The ravages committed by man subvert the relations and destroy the balance which nature has established . . . and she avenges herself upon the intruder by letting loose her destructive energies . . . When the forest is gone, the great reservoir of moisture stored up in its vegetable mould is evaporated . . . The well-wooded and humid hills are turned to ridges of dry rock . . . and the whole earth, unless rescued by human act from the physical degeneration to which it tends, becomes as assemblage of bald mountains, or barren, turfless hills, and of swampy and malarious plains. There are parts of Asia Minor, of Northern Africa, of Greece, and even of Alpine Europe, where the operation of causes set in motion by man has brought the face of the *earth to a desolation almost as complete as that of the moon* . . . (italics mine). The earth is becoming an unfit home for its noblest inhabitant, and another era of equal human crime and human improvidence . . . would reduce it to such a condition of impoverished productiveness, of shattered surface, of climatic excess . . . as to threaten . . . (the) extinction of the species." Such insight, from the middle of the 19th century is mind boggling.

With this kind of heritage, small wonder it is that Vermont's Act 250 is one of the strictest environmental protection laws governing development in the entire United States.

And it is no wonder too, that the State Environmental Commission scrutinizes hydroelectric projects carefully.

Hydroelectric dams can be a great boon to nature, working in consonance with it. They can also destroy nature. Unfortunately, America has been beset by the cult of bigness. It has failed to "think small." Small dams are not nearly as liable to cause environmental disruption and damage as big ones. Small dams such as mine do not destroy farms by flooding farmland, nor do they pose a threat of floods from dam breaks. Hence, dams which do not impound more than 2 acre feet of water are exempt in Vermont from regulation, if they are on streams whose watershed is less than 10 square miles. Such low dams create no obstacles to anadromous fish which often navigate falls much higher. Indeed, on my brook, are waterfalls six feet and more in height, and fish manage to navigate them.

Nonetheless, it is essential that one's project be cleared with state environmental commissions. Vermont's law does not require unreasonable restraints, but attempts a common sense approach to man's richest heritage, a green and bountiful earth which must be treated with reverence if the human race is to survive. If one's hydro project contemplates the erection of a larger dam, fish ladders must be provided.

Great hydroelectric projects such as on the Columbia River or Snake River, have cost hundreds of millions of dollars more just to protect the fish. Yet many fish are killed when sucked into turbines. Others are maimed, or stunned and fall easy victims of predators. It is essential that any project, large or small, take steps to insure the adequate protection of aquatic life.

In considering the suitability of any hydro site, it is wise to obtain precipitation data for one's area. The Vermont State Department of Water Resources provided me with complete data for the past 25 years. Our average annual rainfall is 51.76 inches. Interestingly, fall and winter rainfall/varied very little on average from that in the summer. Indeed, June, on average the driest summer month had more rainfall that September or October in this 25 year span.

Why then, I asked, do streams slow down, or dry up in summer and run much fuller the rest of the year? The answer is to be found in studying Fig. 3-3.

As George Perkins Marsh pointed out so long ago, each tree is a miniature flood control dam. When deciduous trees are in leaf, they soak up an enormous amount of moisture. The transpiration process enables them to return a great deal of moisture to the atmosphere. In summer, probably half the rainfall never becomes stream runoff, because of the trees, and the transpiration process.

Another facet of the hydrologic cycle is: daylight in northern latitudes diminishes in winter to six hours less than occurs in June. As a result, the greatly weakened rays of the sun which is far to the south, fail to evaporate nearly as much water as they do in summer. Winter cloud cover is also a factor.

Many mistakenly believe that once winter sets in in earnest, streams simply stop running because of the ice. If one digs a hole 400 or 500 feet deep, he finds the temperature of the earth to be 45 or 50 degrees F. While there may be deep frost in winter when there is no snow, as soon as snow comes, this natural heat from inside the earth works on the frost, because of the snow insulation, and in short order, all the frost goes out of the earth. Thus, even in the coldest part of the winter, water seeps into the snow blanketed ground because of this natural heat from the earth. Additionally the melting of snow from the rays of the sun, sends more moisture to be soaked up by the ground. The ground water table is replenished, springs are fed, and streams continue to flow, even under ice two feet thick.

I live in the snow belt, where the average snowfall is 120 inches. When days begin to grow longer in Lent, which literally means lengthening of days, (coming from the old Anglo Saxon, Lencten, to lengthen) streams break the bonds of winter and the spring run-off occurs. As trees begin to bud, they help prevent damaging floods and erosion from occurring.

Thus it is, man must work in consonance with nature, and not destroy it. By understanding nature, and working cooper-

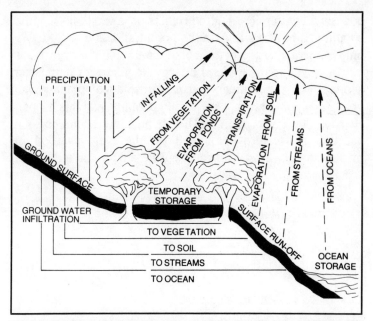

Fig. 3-3. This illustrates what happens when it rains. Bear in mind the great variables between summer and winter. There is six hours more daylight in summer, more evaporation, more transpiration when deciduous trees are in leaf, and conifers require more moisture than in winter. These factors explain why a half inch of precipitation in the dormant season, makes streams run twice as full as they would during the growing season (courtesy of Vermont Dept. of Natural Resources).

atively with it, one's hydroelectric project may be a blessing rather than a curse. So long as one's penstock opening is located two feet or so below the ice, water will flow a half mile and more to the powerhouse, as well as it does in summer. Though friction is small in pvc pipe, it is enough to raise the temperature a degree or two and insure the pipe will not freeze even in the bitterest weather.

DON'T WAIT, DO IT NOW

If you have any idea of building a hydroelectric project, the best advice is: don't wait, do it now. In the first place, costs are rising steadily. In the second place, if you have a "large," small hydro site on your land, someone may beat you to it, even though you own the land. Projects up to 15 MWs are considered to be small hydro projects. While this book is

45

concerned with micro-hydro projects, it is worth noting, that should you have a site with the potential of 200 or 300 kWs, unless you act to protect it, some enterprising entrepreneur may beat you to the Federal Energy Regulatory Commission and take out a preliminary permit for its development. Then you are just out of luck. One person in Maine had this happen. He had a 300 kW location, and before he knew it someone else had the license to develop it. True, the court awarded the owner compensatory damages, but he did not have the site!

Chapter 4

Water Wheels

Probably the first water wheel used by man was made in Egypt. Ancient Egyptians used buckets attached to a wheel to scoop water from the Nile for irrigation. These wheels were turned by animal power. The first improvement on the clay buckets was to put a valve in the bottom, so that on the downward arc, they would fill and offer less resistance as the animal power forced them down into the water. When full, the valve would flap shut, and the cargo of water would be brought up to be used in the fields. Soon it was discovered that the flow or current of the river would itself turn a wheel when paddles were fitted to its perimeter and the bottom section immersed. Thus the first undershot wheel was invented.

In the 19th century, overshot wheels became prevalent, though not entirely supplanting the undershot. In these, water is led through a flume over the wheel and allowed to fall into the buckets on the perimeter of the wheel. The weight of the water in the buckets, plus the small drop involved, help push the wheel around. Too much drop, or velocity however, causes the water to spill from the buckets and thus waste its potential power. The greater the radius of the wheel, the more the weight of the water was magnified in turning the wheel.

Although such wheels turned but a few revolutions per minute, they still capture the imagination and nostalgia of many folk. Fabled in song and story, some modern hydro-power developers seek to recapture the romance of yesteryear by reproducing such relics of a bygone age. See Fig. 4-1.

When the head, or fall of water was not sufficient for a large diameter overshot wheel, the breast wheel often was used. This is halfway between the overshot and undershot wheels. See Fig. 4-2. Water strikes the buckets of the breast wheel about midway between top and bottom, using the weight of the water for a 90 degree segment of arc. While more efficient than the undershot, their efficiency is far less than the overshot, which uses the weight of the water for a full 180 degrees. See Fig. 4-3.

Here and there throughout the country, one still sees an old overshot wheel slowly turning, as it has done for 100 years and more. An old mill in Bernardston, Massachusetts, is still using an overshot wheel and is still operating with an old, rope drive. Here, the power from the wheel is transported several hundred feet by means of a large rope, which in its day was considered quite efficient. See Fig. 4-4.

One variation of the undershot wheel, invented by the Frenchman, Poncelot, uses a concrete sluice very close to the

Fig. 4-1. Mr. N. George of Brattleboro, in restoring the old Bushnell Mill which had burned some years ago, placed an overshot wheel on its side for looks. A modern turbine lies concealed in the basement, turning out power.

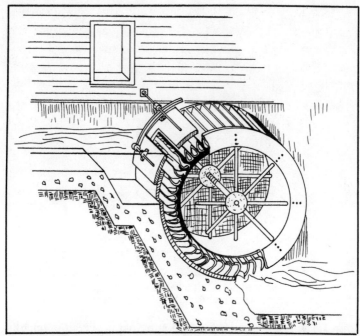

Fig. 4-2. The breast wheel, so called because the water enters the wheel below the top and is kept in the buckets by close fitting breastworks. These wheels operate best with heads of ten feet or less. When water enters well above the shaft, their efficiency can be relatively good, perhaps as high as 65%. (Courtesy of DOE.)

bottom of the wheel, so that most of the water going through will hit the paddles and force them around, without being thrown to the side with the force and weight being wasted. See Fig. 4-5.

In general, all such big wheels are inefficient when compared with modern turbines. Their great bulk militates against them, as well as their slow speed, unsuited to the 1800 rpm required for ac hydro plants such as mine. To obtain the speed necessary, such wheels have to have elaborate gearing, either from the axle, or from a cog wheel working off the perimeter of the wheel itself.

THE PELTON WHEEL

When gold was discovered at Sutter's Mill in California, the great gold rush of 1848-9 was on. Halifax, Vermont, at that

Fig. 4-3. The overshot wheel has a great deal of nostalgia surrounding it. Its efficiency can not be compared with that of a turbine. (Courtesy DOE.)

time a town of less than 1400 people, lost nearly 300 inhabitants to the siren's song of gold.

The problem confronting these miners was: how to get at the gold as quickly as possible. Remembering how they had

Fig. 4-4. The Bernardston, Massachusetts, Grist Mill (The old Dunnel Mill) is still operating today. The mill operates approximately 300 feet from the stream through its rope drive. This picture is of the tower which supports the rope drive, with the mill located across the road. This method of transmitting power from water wheels was common in the 19th century and was quite efficient.

Fig. 4-5. The Poncelot wheel was invented by a Frenchman and is a variation of the old, undershot wheel. The blades of this wheel are curved to give more efficient interaction with the water than a traditional undershot wheel. As with the Breast Wheel, water borne debris poses a problem for these wheels due to the close tolerances of the breastworks which are curved to the shape of the wheel. (Courtesy of DOE.)

harnessed the swift flowing mountain streams of the east, particularly New England, these miners dammed the mountain waters of the west, and with hoses, fashioned "water cannon" to blast silt and dirt away to get at the gold rock.

In the valleys below, they erected large hammer mills to crush the rock, and extract the gold. Recalling their water power from the east, they sent back for large undershot wheels to furnish the power for these hammer mills. But these wheels were too slow, too inefficient to keep up with the mounting piles of ore the water cannon blasted from the hills. To meet this problem, these men invented the hurdy-gurdy. This was the old undershot wheel, but augmented by a water cannon playing on the paddles to make the wheel turn faster. The hurdy-gurdy thus became a crude impulse turbine, being moved in part by the velocity of the water striking its paddles, as well as using the stream current to turn its undershot wheel.

But this was not good enough for a young mining engineer named Lester Pelton. He invented what has become known as the Pelton wheel, an impulse turbine, with a jet, or

51

jets of water hitting cups attached to the perimeter at high speed, forcing the turbine to turn fast and at a high efficiency. See Fig. 4-6.

Pelton however was disappointed. His invention meant scrapping all the present equipment, something the mill owners were loathe to do. But Pelton persevered. He patented his invention. Patiently he demonstrated how his new impulse turbine would develop twice the power of the ponderous old hurdy-gurdys. It was far smaller as well. To market his idea, Pelton formed the Pelton Water Wheel Company. Slowly gathering influence, then gaining momentum and rapidly growing, Pelton saw his fledgling company become a giant, selling its product all over the world.

Unfortunately for the Pelton Company however, America's cult of bigness in the electric utility business took over. Large generating stations, powered by cheap oil multiplied. The Pelton Water Wheel Company fell on hard times. It finally ceased to operate in 1954. Giant power had done it in.

Today however, with oil no longer cheap or plentiful, a new company has been formed. It is called Small Hydroelectric Systems and Equipment of Arlington, Washington. Taking Pelton's original idea, this firm is manufacturing *Pelech hydraulic turbines* and hopes to duplicate in the present energy crisis what Pelton did for the '49ers in the last century.

Telling the story of Pelton's success, Small Hydroelectric Systems Company narrates how Pelton won the miners. The end result was a small, neat hydraulic turbine built in San Francisco, California, which replaced all the hurdy-gurdys as fast as the mining operators could buy them. The young Pelton Water Wheel Company made a range of turbines from 48 inches to a tiny 6 inch one. Many of these old water wheels are still running after 100 years. Pelton went out of business when the need for small hydro equipment was just about nil.

"Still, in the years before 1954, the Pelton Company had covered the world with its equipment. The small micro-hydro of those days was of dc vintage. A few small ac plants were built, but they never sold well, because they needed an operator and a Woodwards governor. Since people just

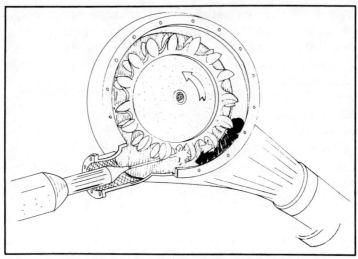

Fig. 4-6. The Pelton wheel operates at high efficiency. Many Pelton wheels have two or more nozzles, so that the flow may be regulated, either for the power needs, or for the stream's flow. (Courtesy DOE.)

wanted lights, they went with dc.

"Then, low cost diesel-electric sets came out, these automatic plants produced ac power with just a push of the start button and used diesel oil, which was very cheap at the time. Those diesel-electric sets immediately replaced the old dc water plants. Only the old ac water powered plants kept running: they worked, and they ran for free. . .."

Besides this Small Hydroelectric Systems Company, in Washington State, there are other firms springing up. Independent Power Developers of Noxon, Montana is one. The James E. Leffel Co. of Springfield, Ohio, has long been in the small turbine manufacturing field. There is also the fine old English firm of Gilbert, Gilkes and Gordon, whose North American representative is Harry McKay, P.O. Box 488, Port Colborne, Ontario, L3K5X7. In its literature, Gilbert, Gilkes and Gordon, Ltd. writes: "(We) are now the only company in Great Britain prepared to manufacture small water turbines, and who still have experienced personnel with the ability to advise."

In one pamphlet, the company attempts to save the time of its engineers from the many inquiries about hydro potential by giving the formula so that one may calculate for himself the potential of any stream. It says: "The output at the generator terminal is roughly calculated from the following formula.

$$kW = \frac{H \times Q}{660} \times 0.82 \times 0.746$$

H = Net head in feet

Q = Quantity in cubic feet per minute

660 = Constant

0.82 = For all practical purposes generator efficiency of units from 5 to 25 kW

0.746 = Conversion factor, brake horsepower to kilowatts

Gilbert, Gilkes and Gordon's wheels for small hydro, bearing the trade name "Hydec" are impulse wheels, that is, they use the kinetic energy, or velocity of the water through a nozzle to strike the cups of the turbine, just as the Pelton wheel did. While there have been some improvements to the Pelton wheel, notably the Turgo impulse wheel, as mentioned by Dermot McGuigan in his excellent book: "Harnessing Water Power for Home Energy," this Gilbert, Gilkes and Gordon Hydec unit essentially is a Turgo impulse wheel.

LOW HEAD WHEELS

Pelton wheels operate best on heads over 50 feet. Two types of wheels which operate efficiently on heads of less than 20 feet are the propeller turbine and the Ossberger cross flow turbine. The Ossberger is an unusually versatile wheel, capable of being used in a wide range of both head and flow. The Ossberger, built originally in Germany, and now in the United States can be used, according to literature on heads as low as one meter. See Fig. 4-7.

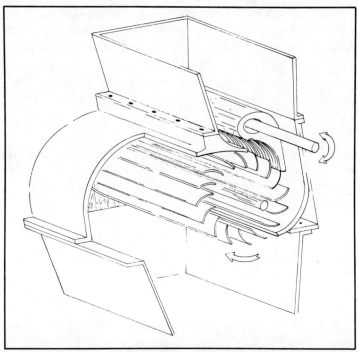

Fig. 4-7. The Ossberger turbine can operate on heads of less than 20 feet. They can be used on heads as low as one meter. Admirably adapted to various heights and flows, they are a versatile type wheel widely used today (courtesy DOE).

THE REACTION TURBINE

The most usual type of a reaction turbine is a Francis turbine. Used often in large installations with heads from 50 to 1000 feet, this workhorse turbine has proved its value for over nearly three quarters of a century at the Vernon, Vermont hydroelectric dam. See Chapter 2, Fig. 2-4.

Reaction turbines differ from impulse wheels in that not just blades or cups struck by the kinetic energy of the water provide the motive power, but all "react" to the flow, each pulling its share of the load. Thus, velocity as well as volume are employed. In this Francis turbine the vanes are called wickets.

THE CENTRIFUGAL PUMP AS AN IMPULSE TURBINE

From his knowledge of the similarities of pumps and turbines, both practical and theoretical, Dr. Kleinschmidt believed that a pump, properly sized to both flow and head could run backwards and serve as a turbine with very little loss in efficiency, as compared to a Pelton wheel. To prove that belief Steve was interested in directing my project. His reasoning was: pumps are mass produced. Turbines are custom made. Hence, pumps have a cost differential greatly in their favor. Pumps are readily available from stock for the most part; turbines are not.

Because Worthington could provide immediate delivery of the proper pump to fit the specifications of my site, we bought it. It was one with a 4 inch intake, and a 3 inch outlet. By turning it around, and using the three inch side as inlet, we had a turbine.

In discussing Dr. Kleinschmidt's idea that a pump would serve as a turbine, if it were simply run backwards, I had many knowledgeable people tell me it would not work. One said: "A pump is a pump, not a turbine. If it were, it would be called a turbine." Quite irrefutable logic, save for the fact that language is at best an inexact instrument for expressing ideas.

To answer this objection, Steve called my attention to the literature put out by some pump manufacturers, extolling this very feature when their pumps were used in skyscraper air conditioning systems. Once water is pumped to the rooftop cooling towers, and trickles down through the cooling vanes, it then falls directly back to the basement. This fall of hundreds of feet is harnessed, enabling the system to recover at least 50 percent of the energy expended to pump the water up to the roof. The same pumps, running in reverse, became turbines.

Later, Worthington Pump was to send me a research paper indicating it was aware of this capacity of its pumps. Sulzer Bros., of San Francisco, California also sent me a brochure describing its "Reverse Running Pumps as Energy Recovery Turbines." Sulzer listed the advantages and disadvantages of this idea. According to its study, it found that the peak efficiency of reverse running pumps is usually lower than turbines. Our experiment, and Worthington's studies disagree with this.

To test his theory Steve machined a drum to fit over the end of the jackshaft which was attached to the pump by means of a flexible coupling. He used a jackshaft because he feared the bearings of the pump might not be able to withstand the radial strain imposed by the belts to the generator. The jackshaft was securely fastened to two hardwood (rock maple) blocks, embedded in concrete and tied down by lag screws. See Fig. 4-8.

Steve then made a Prony brake from two hardwood blocks shaped as brake shoes to clamp over the drum. These were tightened by a spring loaded screw to increase the friction, or load. On top of the upper shoe was a two foot arm, made from a piece of 2 × 4 with a right angle iron bracket which would rest on one end of an old fashioned Fairbanks balance scale. There were not enough weights to match the load so we solved that by using a "keg of nails" and then weighing it.

As Steve tightened the screw to increase the friction, the power house filled with smoke, despite liberal dousing of the shoes with water to cool them. Meanwhile, with a revolution counter, we measured the speed of the pump in revolutions per minute. Thus, through these measurements it was found that 22 pounds was required to balance the load and maintain

Fig.4-8. Jackshaft showing bearings and flexible coupling (courtesy of Worthington Group. Photo by Allen Gill).

the proper speed. Steve determined we had just about the same efficiency as a Pelton wheel would have for this installation.

Calculating the thrust, Steve found we had 14½ brake horsepower and that would give us about 10 kilowatts. One horsepower equals 746 Watts, or 0.746 kilowatts. Multiplying 14½ by that, gives 10.8 kW. To be conservative however, Steve felt that 10 kW was a reasonable figure. If we ran 24 hours a day, that would mean 240 kWh (kilowatt hours), or 7200 kWh for a 30 day month.

WORTHINGTON'S PUMP RESEARCH

My first communication with the Worthington Group of the McGraw-Edison Co. was to ask permission to use illustrations from the pump catalog for this book. Numerous letters and telephone calls ensued. I told Worthington what I had done, and what I was doing. The result was that Mr. Cecil Thrash, the Manager of Public Relations at the Worthington Group asked me to put together an article for his in-house publication: *Power And Fluids.*

Worthington had known for years of the capacity of its pumps to run in reverse as turbines. They had not known of Steve's very clever way of governing the load to obtain 60 cycle current, by simply using an induction motor, which when run about 60 rpm faster than its rated speed, it would automatically produce 60 cycle current.

I mentioned the one drawback that Steve and I found: A pump, functioning as a turbine, does not have the flexibility of a Pelton wheel to run on reduced amounts of water. My pump, rated at one cfs will run and turn out some electricity, perhaps 2 or 3 kilowatts, when there is low water. The efficiency drops off rather rapidly. One notices the tail water becomes very milky when there is insufficient water to run at full power, and air mixes in with the water. The lessened weight on the blades of the pump makes it less efficient.

Imagine my delight, and surprise to receive a telephone call from Mr. Thrash, and then a letter which read in part: *Dear Mr. Butler:*

As we discussed on the telephone, the plans are shaping up to deliver the new pump to you Friday, September 4. Larry Shafer (of our engineering Department, Taneytown, Maryland) will be in touch with you to find out the exact directions to reach your home.

They are still working out the best pump model to meet your requirements of ½ cfs at approximately 200 feet of head. Apparently it could be any one of several pumps and our engineers are determining which will be the optimum model . . .

I enclose a paper on hydroturbines written by some of the engineers at Worthington. I thought it might be of intereste to you . . .

Signed, Cecil Thrash, Manager, Public Relations.

Indeed it was of interest. Steve Kleinschmidt just happened to spend the night with me the day I received this material. I showed the research to him.

"This is wonderful," he exclaimed, "This will take the guesswork out of finding the right pump. You know, most any pump will turn a shaft. It is finding the right one for maximum efficiency that is tricky. I want a copy of these drawings," he said. "This is what I dug out, the hard way."

"Now," continued Steve, "you can hook up your ½ cfs pump, run it in low water, and when there is sufficient flow, you can run both it and 1 cfs and generate 15 kilowatts.

Friday, Sept. 4, 1981, Cecil Thrash and Larry Shafer arrived. Alas, August, 1981 had continued the 2 year drought we had suffered. Sections of Vermont, mostly in the north had had rain. But we were very dry. The Hartford Connecticut Traveler's weather service reported that Hartford had suffered its second driest August in the 140 years of records, getting just over one-half inch of rain all month. I didn't have enough water to have the pump running when my guests arrived. There was enough to run the generator for only 15 minutes and show them how it operated: no cavitation, no noise, just the smooth efficient hum of electric generation. The watt hour meter showing how much power was going

59

back into the utility line was racing around at 20 revolutions a minute. Obviously I was generating the full 10 kW. Larry's comment was: "This is wonderful!"

After lunch, Larry told me: "I am running tests on all our pumps. I have found they will work as turbines for any head over 20 feet."

Because obtaining the proper sized pump for one's location is important and so that all may see the performance characteristics of these pumps, I asked Larry and Cecil for permission to include Larry's research paper in this book (see Appendix A).

That Worthington is in earnest about using its pumps as turbines is attested to by Worthington's research in this field. Its pumps are available as turbines from 20 feet to 1000 feet of head. In some instances, it can supply pumps for heads as low as 10 feet.

Chapter 5

Obtaining Alternating Current from an Induction Motor

Every small hydroelectric equipment manufacturer whose literature I have read has used some type of governor to regulate the frequency of the alternating current produced by his equipment. Dr. Kleinschmidt's knowledge of electrical theory told him it is possible to use an induction motor as a generator which would automatically accomplish this end: producing current synchronous with one's utility without any other regulation. An induction motor is brushless. When its rotor revolves in the magnetic field set up in the stator by exciting it with 60 Hz, it has to induce 60 cycle current, by the very nature of induction.

Old, second hand induction motors can be had very cheaply. If their bearings have been properly lubricated, they will last indefinitely. When I start my rig by opening the gate valve, the pump-turbine revs up to perhaps 3600 rpm. Immediately when I push the start button, and the generation load comes on, it slows down to about 1800 rpm, which is about 60 rpm faster than the motor would run when it was used as a motor. And when the water pressure falls, through lack of water, so that there is not enough power coming from the pump-turbine to turn the motor-generator, a pressure switch cuts the current to the stator so the motor does not then run as a motor, as it would normally do.

Hence, without a battery bank, but using my utility as the "bank" to return my surplus power when I don't need it, I return energy for others to use, and utilize a non polluting, renewable energy source for the benefit, not only of myself, but for others as well.

These two basic ideas: the use of a pump-turbine, the use of an induction mill motor, can revolutionize the small hydro field and add a significant dimension to America's electrical energy production. Up until now, few have realized this relatively simple solution to the problem of producing alternating current.

THE HISTORIC DEBATE:
ALTERNATING VERSUS DIRECT CURRENT

When the age of electrical energy first dawned, there was a battle over the kind of current utilities would supply: alternating, or direct. Edison stood almost alone in his advocacy of direct current, current which flows in one direction, alternating current on the other hand, rapidly alternates in direction, with positive and negative charges alternating many times a second. Edison built the Pearl St. station in New York City to generate direct current. Eventually however, direct current lost out to alternating current because at usual voltages, there is less line loss during transmission.

In 1891, S.Z. Ferranti designed an alternating current power station (in England) which proved the contention of almost all the electrical engineers on the continent of Europe that normal high voltage alternating current could be transmitted more efficiently than direct current. Two years later, when alternators were installed in the first generating station at Niagara Falls, it was clear that alternating current would win out in America too. Though frequencies of 25,50, and 60 cycles per second have been used in Europe and America, the standard frequency in America today is now 60 cycle, or 60 Hertz.

INDUCED CURRENTS

To understand how an old 20 horsepower induction mill motor can serve as a generator requires a little explanation of how electricity is produced. Electricity can be produced in several ways: chemically as in batteries, both wet and dry cell; by sunlight with photovoltaic solar cells; by pressure in piezoelectric crystals used in phonograph pick-up arms, and finally, by magnetism. Michael Faraday discovered in 1837 how electric currents could be induced by using a magnetic field.

Almost everyone is familiar with the way iron filings arrange themselves on a sheet of paper when a permanent magnet is passed underneath. See Fig. 5-1 and 5-2. Faraday found that a wire, moving in such a magnetic field would itself induce an electric current by simply being moved in that field.

A rudimentary generator consists in a single loop of wire rotated in such a magnetic field. As the wire cuts the magnetic lines of force, current is induced. And, every time the wire turns 180 degrees, the direction of the flow of that induced current changes. See Fig. 5-3.

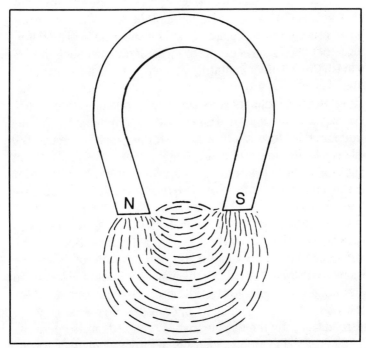

Fig. 5-1. This illustrates the magnetic lines of force from one pole of a horseshoe magnet to another (courtesy, Goodheart-Willcox, Co.).

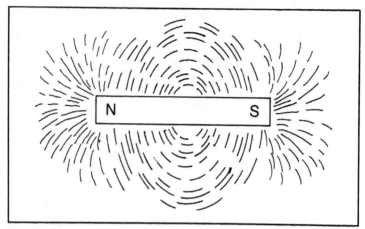

Fig. 5-2. Similarly, an iron bar magnet exhibits the same pattern, which placed under a sheet of paper on which iron fillings have been sprinkled. When the sheet is gently tapped, the filings form patterns along the lines of force (courtesy, Goodheart-Willcox, Co.).

Direct current and alternating current motors have many wires wound both in the stators and the rotors, so that many lines of magnetic force are cut as the rotor spins. The difference between a direct current operation is that such motors have a timer, or commutator, which reverses the direction of the current every time the rotor turns 180 degrees, so that the flow of current remains constant in one direction. Alternating current motors do not have a commutator and the current therefore, alternates, reversing polarity each 180 degrees. There are of course, many types of direct current motors as well as alternating current motors. In practice, it has been found best to have more than one coil for each pole of the field. The motor I have, is thus a three phase motor with three sets of armature coils which may be used separately to supply electricity to several electrical circuits. Because the principles on which a motor, or generator are built are the same, with the rotor cutting the magnetic lines of force set up by the stator, generators and motors are in a sense, interchangeable. A motor may be operated as a generator, when turned faster by the turbine than is required for its operation as a motor. Thus, it becomes a generator, supplying current, rather than using current. Structurally, motors and generators are the same. Each has the same constituent parts: electromagnets, and armatures, and in the case of direct current motors, commutators and brushes.

Electromagnets are made by winding wire around a soft iron core. When current passes through the wire, it becomes a magnet. When it ceases, the magnetism stops except for a very small residual amount. See Fig. 5-4.

Magnetism creates both attraction, and repulsion. When the current passes from one brush into the coil, and back out the second brush, the magnetic field of the coil opposes that of the magnetic field of the electromagnet. The repelling action of like poles makes the rotor or armature start to turn. As the rotor turns, its north pole is attracted to the south pole of the magnet. Just as the two unlike poles are about to line up, the commutator reverses direction of the polarity, and the rotor continues to spin. When there are many magnets in the rotor and stator, the pulsations smooth out and the motor runs smoothly.

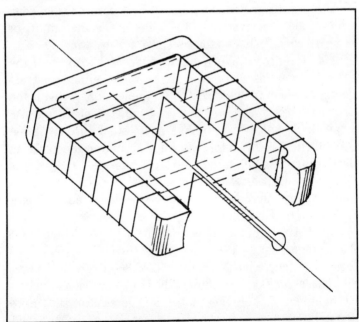

Fig. 5-3. This sketch of a rudimentary motor shows the principle of all motors. As the rotor, in this case, a single loop, rotates in a magnetic field, the magnetic lines of force are cut, and current is produced.

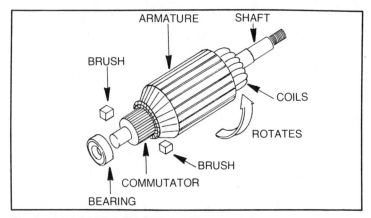

Fig. 5-4. Armature and commutator assembly of a direct current generator. The commutator is actually a type of sliding switch which turns the current around so that it always flows one way, or directly. It consists of many segments of copper, insulated from each other, with brushes to pick up the electricity and keep it flowing in one direction (courtesy of Goodheart-Willcox, Co.).

INDUCTION MOTORS—GENERATORS

An induction motor (see Fig. 5-5) uses neither commutator, nor brushes. Its rotor spins inside the stator, or "squirrel cage." This stator consists of many windings on a laminated steel core. When the current ceases to excite it, the motor, or generator immediately ceases to either run, as a motor, or generate electricity as a generator. As with the stator, the rotor is also made of laminated steel and has copper bars which fit into slots in its steel core. It is the magnetic field of the stator, when it is excited and becomes an electromagnet which turns the rotor. It is when the rotor is turned by mechanical energy, in this case, the energy of falling water, and runs faster than it would as a motor, that it becomes a 60 Hz generator.

With large motors it is customary to wind them as 3 phase units. That is, a complete magnetic cycle is every 120 degrees, rather than the full circle of 360 degrees. Hence, each phase turns out one third of the power available. Such an arrangement makes the motor, or generator run more smoothly.

One problem which confronts such a three phase operation is, to balance the load on each leg of the generator. This is

Fig. 5-5. A cutaway view of an induction motor (courtesy of Westinghouse).

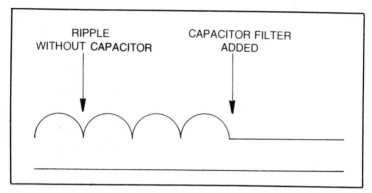

RIPPLE
WITHOUT CAPACITOR

CAPACITOR FILTER
ADDED

Fig. 5-6. When a capacitor filter is added to a circuit the current smooths out-eliminating surges.

accomplished by means of a device called a capacitor. Capacitors smooth out the pulsations, as shown in Fig. 5-6.

Capacitors consist of two or more plates, with an insulator, or dielectric between them. The ability or capacity of a capacitor to store electricity depends on the size of the plates, the distance between them, and the character of the insulating materials. A capacitor not only smooths out the current and helps "balance" the three phases; it also helps protect the system from sudden surges or overloads.

When the generating speed of the turbine slows down so that it no longer turns the motor fast enough to generate electricity, that is, about 1800 rpm in this case, the generator will cease to generate, and will run as a motor, then draw current from the utility. To prevent this there is an automatic pressure switch so that the field will no longer be excited below the charging speed. A pressure switch is mounted on the turbine just before the water enters the wheel.

The pressure switch may be set by starting the turbine at full power, then gradually closing the gate valve until the disc in the watt hour meter is barely turning. When it reaches that stage, the pressure switch should be tightened so that the current to the field of the motor automatically cuts off, thus taking the plant "off line."

Chapter 6

Obtaining Materials
as Cheaply as Possible

All over America, small generating plants have been abandoned because in the past, America has "thought big." Bigness has been equated with "economies of scale," a statement that in many instances simply is not true.

In the 1940s newspapers carried utility advertisements: "Sell us your old scrap generating equipment. It will never be worth more than it is today." Then, oil was cheap and plentiful. Why bother with 500 or 1000 kilowatt plants when one could turn out 500,000 and more oil fired kilowatts? Utilities in New England, when major repairs were called for to dams, or equipment, simply took them out of service. For instance, in my area, a small 500 kW plant at Dummerston, Vermont, on the West River was dismantled, and the dam dynamited. It just didn't pay the utility to bother with it. Such things happened all over New England. As a result, when the oil crisis came, 67 percent of New England's power was oil fired.

Yet despite the abandonment of hydro, some old equipment may still be lying around. The best place to look is in unused mills. Before buying new equipment, it will pay to investigate every possible source of second hand items: junk dealers, war surplus equipment, and second hand electrical equipment.

69

SECOND-HAND INDUCTION MILL MOTORS

Most dealers in second hand equipment have recon-ditioned motors which they would very much like to sell. Often one sees ads in papers for such at exorbitant prices. The price asked may seem good to a novice when compared to the cost of a new motor. But in terms of the market, most are rather high. I read many such ads and saw old mill motors for $500 which I thought seemed to be a good price. But Dr. Kleinschmidt who knew the field, was able to obtain one much more cheaply. Make sure the motor you buy has good coils, which are neither burned nor damaged, and that the bearings are tight. Such a motor, properly lubricated can last almost indefinitely as there are no brushes to wear out. If possible, enlist the help of a friend who is knowledgeable in this field. As with second hand autos, the Latin proverb: "Caveat Emptor," (Let the buyer beware) should be heeded. Do com-parison shopping. Check all sources of equipment in your area. Maybe you can find a motor, or magnetic starter or other devices "for a song."

HOW TO USE "TOM-CAT"

Thomas' Register of Manufacturers, is a massive com-pendium, or catalogue of every known manufacturer of every imaginable kind of device or product in the United States. In the vernacular, it is referred to as "Tom-Cat." If it seems advisable to buy new items, as in the case of pipe, this catalog can save you lots of money. As I indicated earlier, when I wrote 26 manufacturers of plastic pipe, I received bids rang-ing from $5,000 to $19,000.

As replies came in, extolling the virtues of the pipe the various makers produced, I learned a lot about pipe. The best kind of pipe for such a job is slip joint pipe: pipe which has two rubber gaskets inside the bell end of each section, which effectively seal the joint when two pieces are banged to-gether. See Figs. 6-1 through 6-3. I say "banged" because that literally is how the pipe is joined. When the joints are free from grit and dirt and properly aligned they slide easily. Always begin the laying with the bell end first. At the dam, the first bell end received the 6 inch end of the large intake funnel,

Fig. 6-1. Rubber gaskets are placed in the bells of slip joint pipe so that when two lengths are joined together a tight seal is made.

at the beginning of the penstock. Such pipe allows a degree or two of curvature at each joint, quite essential when one is attempting to dodge rocks and trees in the woods.

What I did not know when I ordered the pipe was: I had to make allowance for at least six inches or more of overlap as each section was driven together with the previous one. I wound up 200 feet shy, and found to my sorrow, that in the intervening eight months the price had soared from $215 per 100 feet to $265.

THE ART OF SCROUNGING

As one gets into a project of this kind, he finds friends and neighbors very interested and wanting to help. There is a universal fascination, not only with water power, but also of beating the energy crisis.

Some friends will direct you to equipment which is not suitable. I was told of various centrifugal pumps which had been discarded. Others pointed to old well casing which could be bought cheaply. Under the guidance of Dr. Kleinschmidt however, I avoided some of the pitfalls which a novice might fall into. Although my new pump, with a capacity of 1 cfs was the most costly single piece of equipment I bought, it was far less than a custombuilt turbine.

When it came to finding an old 6 inch gate valve which we put on the line just before the turbine in the powerhouse

Fig. 6-2. The bevelled end of each 20 foot section fits into the bell end thus insuring a tight fit because of the two rubber gaskets.

Steve had the answer. Years ago, he had worked for a large paper company. He knew where there was an old six-inch valve, full of rust but capable of being cleaned up and put into service. A new valve would have cost about $1500. This one was free except for our labor of scraping the rust off it.

Again, when it came to finding poles to string the wire between the powerhouse, and my home, I found an inexpensive source, and a source which is undoubtedly available to many other rural residents who contemplate similar installations. The Vermont Electric Co-op has a policy of making used poles, which it replaces periodically, available to mem-

Fig. 6-3. Holding a piece of two by four across the end of the pipe, the sledge hammer drives it into the end of the section already laid. It is essential that all grit is removed from both the bell and the bevelled ends before banging them together.

bers for the nominal charge of $10 a pole, or $12.50 delivered. Thus, for the price of $25, I had my poles, and Bud Bemis set them with his backhoe. Total cost of erecting the two poles: $125! The co-op charges $500 a pole to set new ones! Since these poles were creosoted under pressure 40 years ago, and since we did not need them quite so high as on the Co-op lines, we cut off the 5 feet which had been in the ground, and they should serve for another 40 years.

There are just over 1000 Rural Electric Cooperatives throughout America. This source of good used poles should be available to almost anyone who is interested in building his own hydro.

When I went to the junk yard to obtain reinforcing rods for the cement in the dam, I found the folks at the yard so interested in what I was doing, they gave me a bargain on the rods.

After the plant was in the home stretch, and we were wiring it up, Bud Bemis, the President of the nearby municipally owned, Village Electric Co. said: "We have some wire we are not using, because we don't use that size anymore. It would be just right for you, and if you want it, we can sell it to you at cost, which several years ago, was a lot cheaper than it is today." So I had my tri-flex wire, again at a substantial saving.

Because Steve Kleinschmidt was so interested in making the project work, he also scrounged equipment: not only the gate valve, but lights for the alarm control circuit, and other items too numerous to catalog. From all this, it is apparent: if you tell folks what you are doing, you will find unexpected offers of help from many quarters.

Chapter 7

Building the Dam
and Laying the Pipe

To build a dam where access by truck is easy is a far different situation than I faced. To obtain the head we needed meant going up a wooded trail. It is a lovely trail, negotiated quite easily by my tractor with half tracks, after the usual five feet of snow has been broken by a bulldozer. But for a ready-mix cement truck? Impossible. At the top I had to cut a road 300 feet through the woods to the dam site. Thus, we had nearly three quarters of a mile to negotiate as best we could.

GETTING READY

To get a backhoe down to the brook was a herculean task. The hill was so steep Bud had to chain the backhoe to his bulldozer, which one of his sons drove. Without this precaution he feared he might get to the brook much too fast! The first job the backhoe had to do was to move enough boulders so that the backhoe could be positioned in the stream to clear the rocks away from the dam site. Even with this big backhoe, it was a difficult task. Its teeth scraped and chattered as unwilling rocks finally gave way to its persistent pull and grudgingly rolled out of the way.

Finally, after much grating and slipping, Bud had as many rocks moved as he could. As his son Randy and I watched his dexterity with that massive instrument, we marvelled how he could nudge one rock, shove another, and scoop up great shovelfuls of silt, sand, and gravel.

Finally the excavating was accomplished, and once again, came the fun of dragging the backhoe up the hill, its own engine roaring at full throttle, as well as the heavy bulldozer whose powerful tug finally won the day and the hoe was once more at the top.

BUILDING THE DAM

Once we were ready to start on the dam, I felt we had made progress. Since ready mix concrete was out of the question, we resorted to more primitive methods. I had an old Sears cement mixer, purchased 25 years ago when we first came to Vermont. An old David Bradley garden tractor had turned it for many years. I hoped it was good for another long workout. But first we had to get supplies to the dam site: lumber for the forms, sand and gravel, and cement had to be brought in each day.

I obtained lumber from a local mill: undressed, which gave the sheathing boards a thickness of a little more than an inch, and 2 × 4s which were two by fours, and not 1½ × 3½. Having had experience with cement work in the past, I realized the importance of building the forms strong enough to hold the weight of freshly mixed concrete. I set the 2 × 4s 16″ on center, made the front wall of the dam almost perpendicular, while slanting the downstream wall so that the base of the dam was three feet thick, while at the top, it tapered to 10 inches.

I placed the headworks of the penstock, the place where water is taken off to run to the powerhouse as close to the near side of the brook as I could so that the pipe running from the dam would not be in the streambed, and in danger from spring freshets.

To build the headworks for the penstock, I first had a local sheet metal firm make a large funnel, two feet across at the mouth, tapering to six inches at the other end, which would fit into the bell end of the pvc piping. I then built the form for the headworks in the shape of a box, two feet out from the front wall of the dam. When building the headworks, one should make a slot at the mouth of the penstock in which he may slide a piece of 2 foot by 4 foot plywood, which will act as a stop, cutting off the water flow if it is necessary to shut the plant down, or make repairs to the penstock. In front of the slot for the plywood stop, there must be a slanting receptacle for the trash rack. Fortunately, my community is still blessed with the services of an old time village blacksmith, so I have a 2 foot by 4 foot trash rack made out of inch iron bars, with inch spacings. In front of this, I placed another frame, this time of wood, covered by quarter inch mesh hardware cloth, to keep small twigs, stones, and other debris from getting into the pump-turbine and injuring it. See Figs. 7-1 through 7-9.

The bottom side of the funnel should be at least a foot above the stream bed, and the top covered by at least 1½ feet of water. Positioning the funnel in this way not only helps prevent debris from being sucked into the penstock, it will also help avoid anchor and slush ice from clogging it. Once the top of the pond is frozen over, water should continue to flow, in normal New England winters, well insulated by the ice and snow cover above.

USING A CHAIN SAW FOR FORM BUILDING

With no electricity available to run my electric saw, the only other power tool available was my chain saw. With a

Fig. 7-1. Bud Bemis is the "Man with the Hoe." The only thing this picture does not show is the noise of the bucket's teeth as they chattered and scraped, trying to dislodge the rock.

Fig. 7-2. Randy Bemis pulling Bud and the backhoe up the hill, out of the brook. Without the crawler bulldozer, the backhoe could never have gotten back out of the brook bed.

sharp chain, this served very well. It was so much faster to saw the green lumber this way, than by a hand saw, that I willingly put up with the slight inaccuracies it made.

Once the framework of the forms was in place, and the sheathing on the upstream side we put one course of sheathing on the downstream side and then we were ready to begin to pour. To make sure the ends of the form would not splay and make a "hog" as builders call such bulges, we carefully anchored the ends with rocks from the streambed.

Fig. 7-3. Gravel was brought to the site by truck. My old cement mixer did a valiant job of mixing the tons of concrete for the dam.

Fig. 7-4. Wet concrete is so heavy it is essential that the dam forms be well braced. Note the funnel to the right side of the framework of the dam.

THE TRACTOR GIVES UP THE GHOST

Back in 1954, I had bought a used David Bradley Garden Tractor. It had mixed hundreds and hundreds of bags of cement for a dam which I had built on the brook in 1956 for fire protection and a swimming hole. It also mixed fifty bags for cementing the floor and walls of the house cellar, woodshed, garage, and other chores too numerous to men-

Fig. 7-5. The dam form takes shape. Note the headworks of the penstock to the far right with the funnel on the bank not yet in place. The penstock must be to the side, and go to dry land as soon as possible so that spring freshets won't wash it away.

Fig. 7-6. The concrete is being poured by my two helpers. Note the reinforcing rods inside the form. The downstream side of the form is slanted to prevent toppling in high water.

tion. It had always performed nobly. This time, after it ran under its own power up the hill, it suddenly decided the time had come to quit. It wouldn't work. It ran all right when it ran by itself, but put a load on it, such as turning the drum of the mixer, and it just died.

Was it finished, I wondered? After all, more than twenty five years service with no problems! Hadn't it earned a rest? I called another friend, Larry Crosier, master mechanic and a friend of many years, and told him the trouble.

Fig. 7-7. After the left side of the dam was complete, the stream was diverted to that side, so that the right side could be poured, with the water running through the gate in the middle.

79

Fig. 7-8. Note the six inch penstock with the funnel at the end. After the head-works of the penstock were completed, the bell of the first length of penstock was joined to the funnel in the concrete box of the penstock.

"Sounds like points to me," he said. "When was the last time you put new ones in?"

"Darned if I know," I replied, "I've never put them in."

"Okay," said Larry, "I'll come over. Can I drive my old jeep truck up through the woods?"

"If it has enough clearance." I said.

It did have enough clearance, and Larry's diagnosis was correct. New points, and the old rig was ready for another 25 years.

POURING THE DAM

To ensure that the concrete would be strong, I used a rich mixture: four parts sand and gravel (a very good bank run grade) to one part cement. Good cement, I had learned by experience, must not be too wet. Yet when it is dry it is difficult to work down into the forms. If it is not tamped sufficiently the results are poor (cement that is honeycombed with gravel showing and hence porous). I cannot emphasize this aspect of dam building enough. No matter how much you tell workmen to tamp the mix down so as to completely compact the aggregate, they just won't do it enough. As a result, when the forms were taken off, I had to do numerous repair jobs with my mason's trowel, to make the faces of the dam tight.

REINFORCING BARS

Although I had built my fire protection dam on the brook near the house in 1956 without reinforcing bars and it has not cracked I felt it imperative that this dam be made of reinforced concrete. For one thing, the swimming pool or fire protection dam has its gate open in winter and thus does not have to withstand the pressure of ice against it. The power dam, on the other hand, will have such stresses. I placed longitudinal reinforcing bars every foot and perpendicular bars also spaced a foot apart.

Talking over dam construction with Dr. Kleinschmidt, he stressed the need of not making the dam any less than the three feet width at the bottom. Indeed, if such a dam is to be higher than mine, it would be wise to widen its base at least in the same ratio, width to height.

SLUICING THE STREAM

Since the stream was flowing when the dam was poured, our first job, before we mixed any cement, was to divert the water to one side. I did this upstream where the rock formation made it relatively easy to channel the water to the penstock side. Having done this we were then free to pour the other side and the floor of the gate. The gate is four feet wide, with slots in the concrete to accommodate the 2 × 6 and 2 × 8

Fig. 7-9. In the days before cement, crib dams were the standard construction in Vermont. This old crib dam is in Halifax, on the Greem River. Now in disrepair, such dams as these provided the water power for New England in the Industrial Revolution.

81

planks in the gate. Putting a bolt in each plank makes each much easier to hook out particularly in winter.

In making the slots extra pieces of clapboard tapered from a feathered edge to half an inch, make good wedges to hold the 2 × 4s used for the slot channels. Greasing these 2 × 4s also helps when taking them out once the cement has hardened. Without such precautions, it becomes a chore to remove them.

After the far side of the dam was poured (with the floor of the gate in place) I then diverted the stream back so that it ran through the open gate and thus we were able to pour the remainder of the dam.

LAYING THE PIPE

Because of Vermont's rocky terrain, both Steve and I thought that we would have to do some rather extensive bridging if the penstock were to be laid on grade. Shortly after the dam, there is a bowl shaped bank on the side of the defile leading down to the brook that all but defied pipe laying save through the use of cedar posts and cradles for bridge work. But that would mean more problems with freeze ups, less permanence, and more danger from animals and humans. The reason we had to confront this bowl was: we had to get up out of the stream bed as quickly as possible. If we didn't, spring freshets could well take the whole penstock out.

Bud Bemis was more than equal to the problem. Carefully surveying the situation Bud opined: "I don't know . . . I'll see what I can do." With that, he proceeded to direct his boy Randy on the bulldozer, to cut down the beginning of the bowl, and make a pad on which the backhoe might travel. Then came another surprise. Going back to his pick-up truck, Bud uncovered a transit. With that, he took careful sightings. Yes, he could make it. First he would go as far as he could from the edge of the bowl on the upstream side. Then he would come around and do the same thing from the downstream side. And with the long arm of the backhoe he secured the pipe firmly in the side hill. By the time he got through with the downstream portion, he was digging six feet down, so as to maintain grade, but he did it. No bridging! A masterful job of pipe laying!

At first I had more or less thought I might lay the pipe by hand. The nature of the terrain however, quickly showed that to be impossible. In two weeks, the backhoe had dug a ditch for the pipe, laid it, and covered it over all the way to the meadow. Then it was necessary to bury the pipe two or more feet in case someone should decide he wished to plough the field, he could do so, without disturbing the hydro.

When Steve came to inspect the job he was amazed. "You got a wonderful job, George," he said. "I've seen contractors on sewer jobs charge three times what this cost."

All in all, with cement $3.25 a bag, five yards of gravel $18 and the cost of labor, backhoe hire, and pipe, the dam and penstock cost about $12,000 or about two thirds the cost of the entire project. This ratio of dam cost to the entire project is about average. In my case the 2700 feet of pipe laid was far more than average. See Figs. 7-10 through 7-15.

RECYCLING LUMBER

Lumber, even native undressed lumber is expensive. I paid 22¢ a board foot. Naturally, if the lumber from the dam forms could be salvaged and reused, I wanted to do it. It was a

Fig. 7-10. Laying the penstock around the "bowl" presented problems of keeping it "on grade." To do so, "Bud" had to dig down as far as six feet to keep it from having sags. Once around this problem, the pipe lies just under the earth, barely below the surface.

Fig. 7-11. To keep the pipe on grade, "Bud" Bemis is standing on it in the bottom of the trench while son Randy backfills with the small bulldozer.

job pulling out all the nails we had put into it. I had not realized how many we had used. Before starting, I had stocked up on nails, buying 50 pound cartons of 8, 10, and 16 penny nails. Instead of 70¢ a pound, this way they cost about 33¢ a pound.

I have learned how to pull nails out straight. Tap the nail until the head is out enough to get the claws of a big wrecking bar under it. Pull it out an inch or so, then put a piece of scrap under the bend of the bar, so that it rests on it and when the nail is pulled it will come out straight.

With the scrap lumber from the dam forms, I almost had enough lumber for the powerhouse. It would be covered with

Fig. 7-12. "The Man With the Backhoe", Howard M. "Bud" Bemis a skilled operator of heavy equipment.

Fig. 7-13. Going across the meadow, or hayfield, Bud laid the pipe deep enough so that if someone decides to plough the field, he won't disturb the penstock.

clapboards. No one would see the dirty cement boards. Why waste them?

CRIB DAMS

Should it be impossible to get any mechanical equipment up to a dam site, thus necessitating all cement mixing to be done by hand, another option is available, the construction of a crib dam. Crib dams used to be the only type made on small streams in New England. They are made of huge beams, formed into 12 foot squares, which are then loaded with rock.

Fig. 7-14. Nearing the end of the pipe laying, Bud opens up the last few feet of trench.

85

All manner of material is caught in them, silt, sand, gravel, and they quickly become water tight.

Though crib dams have washed out in unusual floods, generally they have a life of at least 30 years. Many last much longer. One on the North River, just below Halifax, Vermont, in Massachusetts was recently taken out which had been in place for 80 years. Hemlock is the best kind of timber to be used in such dams. If the timbers remain wet, and are not subject to alternate drying out by low water, they will last very well. Other soft woods do not have this quality.

I was so intrigued with this method of construction, which would use native materials readily available, that I almost went the crib dam route. But I didn't have the equipment to cut the hemlocks and saw them into 8 × 8 timbers, nor did I have the time for this laborious process.

BUILDING A CRIB DAM

Should one desire to build a beaver type crib dam, the following illustration, as suggested by Dr. Kleinschmidt should be followed. See Fig. 7-16.

Directions: locate headers about 6 feet apart on centers across the stream. Fill the structure with 4 inch to 12 inch stones before putting on deck. Do not plank the downstream face of the dam. Place large stones at the base of the dam to

Fig. 7-15. The completed dam shows the penstock off to the left, covered over with concrete and rock so as not to wash away in spring floods.

86

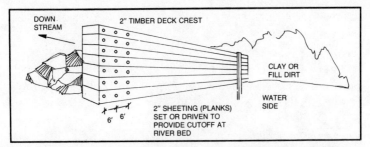

Fig. 7-16. This illustrates how one might build a modern crib dam today.

break up overflow if the dam is on earth and the water flowing over would wash its foundation out. Chink the spaces between the headers and long timbers with small stones and gravel. Timbers should be at least 8 inches in diameter. Pin timbers together with drift pins long enough to go through two timbers and into the third. Pre-drill holes with a 9/16 inch auger bit and use 5/8 inch pins of round hot rolled steel.

Chapter 8

Building the Powerhouse

To place the powerhouse in the best location called for a consideration of several factors. First, it was essential that we obtain the greatest possible amount of head. Second, relative proximity to our house was important. I well remembered winter snow drifts eight and ten feet high. When I thought of the year Mike, our 100 pound Irish Setter, ran straight up the drifts against the sugar house to its cupola, I knew nearness to the house was a prime consideration. One couldn't move far in the average winter, without snowshoes. See Figs. 8-1 and 8-2.

It was essential also, that the powerhouse be located high enough off the stream so that it would not be damaged by spring run-offs. Finally, though not absolutely imperative, it was worth considering: I didn't want to have to string more wire, and set more poles than necessary.

We chose for a location a site on the meadow approximately 20 feet from the brook (immediately behind the sugar house on the other side of the brook). It was unfortunate that it was on the other side but the terrain from the dam down to the powerhouse made it impossible to lay the penstock on the near side. However, I had a good footbridge across the brook, with stringers that wouldn't wear out. After replacing log

Fig. 8-1. In a normal year, snowfall averages 120 inches. The only way one can navigate any distance through it is on snowshoes. But the snow is essential for the hydro to operate. When two or more feet of snow is on the ground, insulating it against the cold, natural radiation enables the snow on the bottom to melt replenishing underground water and making the stream flow briskly even in below zero weather.

stringers several times, I took the old Jeep wagon, went to the east Deerfield railroad yards and saw the foreman. "Can I get a couple old pieces of railroad iron?" I asked.

"Sure" replied Tony, who was in the midst of an after lunch card game in the section house of the yard.

Fig. 8-2. My 18th century Cape Cod Colonial has withstood many an icy blast. Now it is warmed by the mechanical energy of falling water, which is turned into electrical energy by homemade hydro.

89

One of Tony's helpers went with me, picked up one end of a 12 foot rail, and said: "Grab the other end."

I tugged. Nothing happened! Then I planted my feet and pulled in earnest. Finally, my end came up, and somehow I staggered to the Jeep. Though my shoulders seemed separated at the armpits I managed to repeat the process for the second rail, except this time I was quick to get my end up before the railway man. Yes, it was lighter that way!

PREPARING THE FOUNDATION

If one has access to a backhoe or bulldozer, it is a lot easier, quicker, and cheaper in the long run to have the machine do the excavating for the footings for the powerhouse. I had Bud scrape off not only all the top soil, but also several feet of cobblestones. This river valley where I live is the glacial remains of a prehistoric ice age. After the foot of top soil, there is nothing but cobblestones, a situation which provides for excellent drainage for foundations but which is murderous to work on with pick and shovel.

I had Bud go down several feet and grade off a plot about 20 feet square. After I built the forms for the footings in this area, it would be very easy to back fill around the foundation to the required depth and put gravel inside the foundation as high as we needed for the base of the cement floor. Frost heaves in such a situation would be practically impossible.

BUILDING THE FOUNDATION FORMS

Once more the job of building forms confronted me. I had the sharpened 2 × 4s from the dam which I could drive into the earth to anchor the forms plus all the other lumber salvaged from that operation. Given the kind of ground on which I was building I felt footings 2½ feet deep were adequate. Drainage was so good I doubted there would be much problem of frost heaves. Since the foundation was a unit and the coupling between the 6 inch plastic pipe to the steel pipe coming through the foundation allowed for a little flexibility it wouldn't matter if the whole building did rise an inch or two. Given the usual good snow cover, the chances of any movement were small.

I took care to get the forms as square and as level as possible, for the quality and character of the building which I would erect depended on the quality of the foundation. The wall where the penstock enters I set perpendicular to the penstock, so the pipe would come in the middle of the powerhouse, and at right angles to the wall. To use an elbow at the bottom end of the penstock would increase friction loss greatly.

In this wall I left a 12 inch square opening, through which the steel pipe would come which then would be cemented in tightly to prevent any "squirming" of the pipe when water flow was interrupted. With the head I had I estimated the total pressure at the powerhouse to be about 3,000 pounds, and if the pipe were not anchored securely it could spell trouble.

I then had another truck load of cement sand dumped alongside the powerhouse site. With my Ford 2000 tractor I went up to the dam lashed the old cement mixer to its drawbar, and gingerly brought it back down to the powerhouse. By comparison with pouring the dam, mixing the "mud" for the foundation was easy. It went quickly. In two days after I was set up, the job was done. While each side was still green I set two anchor bolts into the concrete so that I could anchor the plate to prevent the building from coming off its foundation in a winter gale.

While the forms were still on the outer walls, or foundation, I used them to help anchor the forms for the trench, or spillway, which was to bisect the middle of the building. The spillway walls were six inches thick. The trench for the spillway was made 24 inches wide and about 18 inches deep. The floor of the powerhouse slants about 6 inches on each side of the trench, so that any water slopping from the spillway, will run back into it.

After the spillway walls were set, I placed 2 × 4s lengthwise, and even with the sides of the spillway. I then had the backhoe fill the sides with gravel, to bring them up so that a floor could be poured, four inches thick. Since this was the first powerhouse I ever built, I would do one thing differently on the next one! I would lower the floor at least a foot, so that I could work on the turbine and other equipment without breaking my back bending over. As it is, by putting on boots, I can stand in the spillway, and work in reasonable comfort. It would be better however to bring the penstock in at least a foot and a half above the floor to make maintenance chores a bit easier. On the wall opposite the penstock, I left an opening approximately two feet by two feet, for the spillway.

Having the penstock come in at floor level, I had to pour the base for the turbine right in the spillway trough, inserting about three feet of six inch pvc pipe at the bottom, to take care of any water coming from the half inch line tapped into the steel pipe before the gate valve. I did this so that when the turbine had to be shut down in winter we could keep water flowing and thus prevent freezeups.

In order to make a solid foundation for the jackshaft and generator I had to take a sledge hammer and break up sections of my carefully laid floor. But this is ahead of the story. I had to finish building the powerhouse before I gave attention to the equipment to be installed in it. See Figs. 8-3 through 8-12.

AN AMATEUR CARPENTER AT WORK

Since hydroelectric installations have a life expectancy of 100 years or almost indefinitely, so long as regular maintenance is kept up, I wanted to build the powerhouse carefully. I

Fig. 8-3. Preparing the forms of the foundation.

Fig. 8-4. Checking the boards.

laid two layers of tar paper on the footings, creosoted the bottom plate of 2 × 8s, and of course set the 2 × 4 wall studs 16 inches on center. Often it was possible to piece together shorter pieces of 2 × 4 salvaged from the dam forms to make the required length of seven feet six inches for the walls. In constructing the framing, I tried as best I could to keep the walls plumb and the building square. The uneven thickness of the undressed lumber provided headaches when trying to make the building completely true. It looks quite "cute" however, and is eminently serviceable. My wife fairly "drooled" over it when it was completed: "It's just like the kind of play house I dreamed of when I was a little girl," she said. "If I had only had such a place to play in then!"

Fig. 8-5. Finishing one side.

The most difficult part of any building, when it is built by one man, is, setting the rafters. For long ones, I don't know how one person can do it. For a small building such as this I found out how. First I set a 2 × 4 on each end of the gable, sticking up in the air six feet, and making sure each was perpendicular with the top plate. The top plate was made of two courses of 2 × 4s. Since the building was 12 × 12 feet, a

Fig. 8-6. The forms are almost completed.

Fig. 8-7. Pouring the concrete.

six foot gable would make an equilateral triangle from the
ridge pole to the top plate. Hence, figuring the angle to cut the
rafters was easy. I cut the first pair to be sure, then set them
butting equally against the ridge pole. Then I proceeded along
the ridge, with rafters every 16 inches. We live in snow
country, and there was no use skimping here. Each wall stud
at the foot of each rafter was tied to the opposite wall by 2 × 4

Fig. 8-8. As the foundation takes shape, Bud and Randy put the finishing touches
on backfilling across the meadow and smoothing the field.

Fig. 8-9. The window in the foundation at the far side of the picture is for the spillway to the brook.

tie rods. When inch planking was then set, I had a building framed to last as long as someone kept a good roof on it.

Though our home has a slate roof, that was too much trouble and expense, so I settled on a good grade of shelf sealing shingles. I had put a similar roof on a shed we call the tractor house more than 25 years ago. With a similar pitch to the roof, they still look to be in excellent condition and I suppose this roof will be equally durable. See Figs. 8-13 through 8-17.

Though the old cement covered boards from the dam and foundation forms of the powerhouse looked unsightly when used to sheathe the powerhouse it didn't make that much

Fig. 8-10. Here I'm filling my cement mixer with another batch of "mud."

Fig. 8-11. The walls for the spillway inside the powerhouse are 6 inches thick, and two feet apart. Note bolts in foundation to anchor plate to it.

difference. First, I covered the whole building with tar paper, then I clapboarded it. The corner posts were made from five inch dressed boards I had in the barn.

Cedar clapboards were simply out of sight, cost-wise. A good grade of pine clapboards was available at half the cost of cedar. And as soon as they were on and their end joints caulked I stained the structure with cuprinol wood stain, which gave it a splendid appearance and tightened up any

Fig. 8-12. Bud Bemis and son Randy drive the last section of pipe together for the penstock.

97

Fig. 8-13. The building takes shape as I set the rafters.

knots which might have a tendency to work out had they not been treated. Before shingling the roof, I installed drip edge, which consists of preformed aluminum strips to cover the edge of the roof sheathing, so as to prevent rot.

By the time I was sheathing the roof I found that I could go much faster, if I obtained some more 12 foot boards rather than have to fit short sections together. One must be careful if shorter pieces are used to make sure joints do not come at the same place on adjacent pieces. See Figs. 8-18 and 8-19.

For windows, I placed barn sash, 2 feet square, just under the top plate, on the penstock and spillway sides. By placing them high, and partially sheltered by the foot overhang of the roof I felt they were less apt to be smashed, than if they were lower down. In the summer, when the powerhouse gets hot, I can take them out to give good cross ventilation for the generator turns out about a kW of heat when it is producing electricity. Such heat, welcome in winter, can cause overheating in summer, if there is not adequate ventilation.

The final job was to build the tail race. I had had Bud dig it out roughly with the backhoe. Now came the task of widening it enough so I could build some more forms and cement the bottom to carry the water back to the brook. By the time I finished the spillway, it was well past the middle of November. June feared that while I was cementing the bottom of the spillway my head sticking up might be mistaken for the hind end of a deer so she insisted I wear a bright orange stocking cap to avoid any mistake. But there was no problem.

Fig. 8-14. After several pairs of rafters are set, the rest is easy.

Fig. 8-15. The building is almost framed.

Steve Kleinschmidt taught me another trick: how to make a water gate that was a good "watergate". By dropping a wood curtain in the tail race at the foundation wall on the inside (to within two inches of the bottom) and then putting a similar baffle several feet on the outside (from the bottom up) one thus formed a watergate so that the waste water running underneath effectively sealed the powerhouse from winter winds, and rodents seeking refuge from winter's cold.

Fig. 8-16. To economize, the author cleaned up the dam boards and reused them for sheathing the building.

Fig. 8-17. While the old cement boards from the dam forms look bad here, they are covered up with tar paper and then clapboards so there is no reason not to reuse them.

If one has never shingled before, a tip can help one obtain a good job. Make triangle like braces with one leg (the leg which will rest on the roof) extending several inches on the up side. To that, nail a piece of roof flashing or any sheet metal several inches long. This metal is then nailed into a course of shingles already laid, high enough so that the next course will cover the holes. As one will see, by placing such triangles every few feet he then can lay two two by eight planks on these supports to make an excellent platform from which to work. See Figs. 8-20 through 8-24.

As I began shingling I first put up a scaffold on the eaves side extending out from the building and about five feet high.

Fig. 8-18. As one sheathes the side of a pitched roof such as this he can nail cleats to the boards to keep his footing.

This enabled me to begin the shingling standing up. Then as I went up the side, I replaced the scaffold on the side of the building with one right under the roof rafters. I then was able to complete the shingling with three cat walks. See Figs. 8-20 through 8-24.

After the sides were done, the top was capped by using thirds of shingles, so as to cover all nails, except at the last shingle at the roof overhang. These nails were covered with roof tar.

Fig. 8-19. Here the sheathing job is almost finished.

Fig. 8-20. As soon as shingling is finished the planks for the cat walks are taken down and the triangles which are fastened under the overlap of the shingles either pulled out with a slating tool or cut with tin snips.

Fig. 8-21. With the roof shingled the powerhouse is nearly completed.

Fig. 8-22. Getting ready to hang the door.

Finally, the catwalks were ready to be dismantled. I used my slating tool, a long hooklike device which enabled me to go under the tab of the shingles, and pull the roofing nails holding the tin piece down. If one prefers, he can snip the tin off as it won't do any harm to leave it if it is cut off so it does not show. The only trouble with this is that the next time one uses his triangles on a roofing job he will have to cut new metal strips

Fig. 8-23. This is how the completed powerhouse looks.

Fig. 8-24. The last part of this job is to cement the spillway from the powerhouse back to the brook.

to replace those he has cut off. To make such triangles, one inch stock, 3 inches wide is adequate. Care must be taken to make sure each triangle is in line with the rest so that the planks rest evenly.

Chapter 9

The Layout of the Machinery

Once the powerhouse was built, the next job was to prepare for the equipment to go into it. As I indicated in Chapter 8, I would recommend that the penstock be brought in higher than mine so as to enable one to work on the equipment without having to stoop over.

BRINGING IN THE PENSTOCK

Once the powerhouse is finished the next job is to bring the penstock in. One may use either cast iron or steel pipe for this connection. The end extending a foot or so inside the powerhouse must have a flange welded on it which can couple with the flange on the gate valve. Be sure the adapter is for the kind of pipe available as adapters for cast iron pipe to plastic will not fit steel and vice versa. This connector is a sleeve with iron rings on either end which can be tightened down by means of long bolts with nuts on both ends (see Fig. 9-1). When these rings are compressed rubber gaskets inside are expanded thus preventing leaks. Do not cement this adapter as it is quite possible that when the water starts flowing one may find himself with a geyser. I did, because I had the wrong kind of adapter. Once equipped with the proper sleeve the leak was fixed and we filled in around the penstock

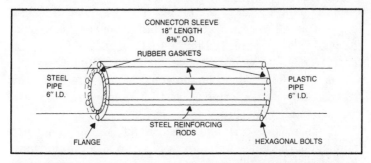

CONNECTOR SLEEVE
18" LENGTH
6⅜" O.D.

RUBBER GASKETS

STEEL PIPE 6" I.D.

PLASTIC PIPE 6" I.D.

STEEL REINFORCING RODS

FLANGE

HEXAGONAL BOLTS

Fig. 9-1. This is the adapter used on the penstock where it changes from plastic to steel pipe. Note: rubber gaskets compress and seal ends when the nuts are tightened.

with sand, easily removed, should another leak occur. Pressure in a six inch pipe after a 225 foot fall approaches 100 pounds psi, or, a total thrust of nearly 3000 pounds, so leaks can happen. It is because of such pressure that it is essential that the iron pipe be firmly anchored in the concrete foundation so that it can not squirm when the water is being turned off or on. This is the reason why a gate valve is necessary (with its worm drive) so that water flow may be regulated very slowly to prevent damage to the penstock and machinery in the powerhouse.

Once the gate valve is in place, the next section of pipe to be connected is an eccentric reducer (a short length of pipe straight on the top edge but slanted on the bottom so that the diameter is decreased from six inches, to three inches to match the turbine inlet).

As indicated previously, the pump when used as a turbine uses the 3 inch orifice as the intake and the 4 inch one as the discharge (exactly opposite from its installation as a pump). To properly mount the pump takes careful preparation. Bear in mind: a pump the size of mine weighs about 250 pounds. It therefore must be securely anchored to a firm foundation if it is to perform as it should.

Having made the spillway two feet wide the entire length of the powerhouse, I was thus able to mount the pump in the center of the spillway, just after the gate valve. First I cut a three foot section of plastic pipe and placed it in the center of the spillway where I wished to mount the pump. Then I carefully built a form to the proper height so that the pump flange would line up with the eccentric reducer flange from the gate valve. I cemented in the metal pieces of foundation from the pump to which its base would be bolted. Once this was done, and the concrete allowed to set several days, my friend Randy Bemis, came down to help move the monster into position and secure it to its base.

A quarter century ago, when Randy's grandfather had built our sugar house, while I was still a preacher in Hartford,

Fig. 9-2. This shows the relative position of the major components of the installation. Beginning in the foreground is the waste water pipe which comes from the 4″ side of the pump. An eccentric expander and a 45 degree elbow give just enough back pressure so that there is no cavitation.

Fig. 9-3. The pressure switch automatically turns the current off, when there is not enough water to turn the motor at generating speed.

Connecticut, I learned his trick: don't lift! Skid! And what you can't skid, use Mr. Archimedes' idea—the pry bar. Amazingly enough, the college boys I had helping me with the dam had never heard of Archimedes and his famous dictum: "Give me a fulcrum on which to rest my lever, and I can move the world."

Randy and I carefully skidded and slowly eased the pump into position. Then we bolted it down to its base and its flange lined up exactly with that of the gate valve. The greatest hurdle had been surmounted. See Fig. 9-2.

Once the pump was in position, the next job was easy, attaching the eccentric expander to the four inch orifice of the pump, to bring the waste water quickly out in a six inch diameter pipe. A 45 degree elbow was bolted to the six inch end and then a short piece of iron pipe attached which I had my blacksmith cut so that its opening was two inches from the floor of the spillway.

In such high head installations as mine the conventional draft tube is not necessary. The eccentric expander and the six inch pipe discharging into the spillway give enough backpressure so that cavitation is no problem and the pump works splendidly with this set-up. See Fig. 9-3.

Iron pipe is heavy. In order not to put an undue strain on the pump I had my blacksmith make two legs which bolted on the flange of the elbow, which then supported it from the floor. Thus, when running, no extra strain is placed on the pump. See Fig. 9-4.

Between each set of flanges, there must be a gasket, so that there are no water leaks. On the pump shaft it is wise that the packing glands are not pulled up so tightly that no water drips through them to cool them. Without a drop or two every second, these glands will overheat and be ruined.

As I indicated earlier the size of the pump one orders must be determined by the head one is harnessing and the amount of water available. If the pipe or penstock is well laid (on grade and without sags) the nomographs referred to earlier will give a good approximation of the power one may expect to obtain.

If water flow varies greatly (as it does in most locations) it often is wise to install two pumps and two induction motors. As I have found out during the current two year drought my plant is often down because I do not have the one cfs needed. By installing a smaller pump I can run in low water. In high water I can run both and generate 15 kW. Only at sites where one uses but part of the available water for his needs, will one unit be suitable for all seasons of the year. The extra cost of a smaller pump and motor is low and the benefits are high.

THE HALF-INCH VENT LINE

Before the iron, or steel pipe is installed through the foundation wall, it is wise to drill and tap it for half inch pipe thread. Remember that half inch inside diameter pipe requires a tap much larger than a half inch. Into these threads a half inch pipe with a gate valve and a flexible copper pipe (bent so as to discharge in the bottom of the spillway) must be fitted. Thus, if the equipment must be shut down in winter, water can still flow in the penstock preventing freezeups.

INSTALLING THE JACKSHAFT

Since the power from the turbine is transmitted to the generator by belts this means that the radial load on the pump shaft may be greater than its bearings are designed to bear.

Fig. 9-4. Pump in foreground, showing the flexible coupling, bearings, and jackshaft.

Hence, it is necessary to couple the turbine by means of a flexible coupling to a jackshaft mounted on two pillow block bearings of sufficient size to take the heavy load the belt drive places on them.

Since this was Dr. Kleinschmidt's "brain child," and it *was* an experimental operation, he machined a jackshaft on his lathe (one and 7/16th inches diameter) and about 21 inches long. Just before the shaft was connected to the flexible coupling he decreased the diameter to 1¼ inches.

Having inveigled John Carnahan into doing the concrete task of breaking up the floor, the next job was to scoop out a hole in the gravel about 12 inches deep, and 17 by 17 inches in size. I then poured a cement base about 4 inches above the floor and placed two hardwood blocks (in this case rock maple) into the cement, lag bolted down, to take the pillow block bearings which were about ten inches apart.

When this work was done, Steve then installed a flexible coupling, a device simulating a universal joint, which would take care of the possible imperfect alignment of the jackshaft with the turbine shaft. See Figs. 9-5 through 9-7.

PREPARING FOR "BIG STEVE"

Since "Big Steve" (my generator) weighs about 500 pounds it was essential that a firm foundation be prepared for

111

Fig. 9-5. Photo of motor-generator showing how it is connected by three matched cog V belts by pulley at end of jackshaft. Jackshaft is used to take strain off bearings in pump. The belt guard is not in place to show layout better.

him. Accordingly, about ten inches from the end of the cement foundation for the jackshaft I built a large 2 foot by 3 foot cement base for the generator. Again, we went down a foot or so into the gravel beneath the powerhouse floor, to make sure the foundation would hold securely.

This base for the generator was brought up level with the top of the footing on which the sill lay and was placed right against the footing. Then I placed two hemlock 8 × 8s (22 inches long) parallel, to accommodate the base on which "Big Steve" would ride. Again these were securely anchored in the concrete. Next, the base was mounted on the 8 × 8s, and we were ready to place "Big Steve" in position.

MOUNTING "BIG STEVE"

Placing 2 × 4s across several of the wall ties, I then rigged my 4 ply block and tackle, put the hook into the eye bolt on Big Steve's top, and we were ready to move him into position. Next came the job of lining up the pulley on Big Steve's shaft with that of the jackshaft. They had to be in line or else the belts would wear. Yet, because of the pressure exerted by the belts as we cranked "Big Steve" up to put more tension on the belts, his pulley inevitably skewed, as the belts kept his front side from moving as fast as the back.

Fig. 9-6. The eccentric reducer diminishes the diameter of the pipe from six inches to three inches as it enters the pump thus greatly increasing its velocity. The reducer is at far left of picture, with pump just behind the flexible coupling (photo by Allen Gill courtesy Worthington Group).

To remedy this condition Steve made a belt-tightener (two hardwood blocks on either end, connected by an adjustable shaft in the middle). As one tightened the nut the shaft expanded thus increasing the tension on the belts to the desired level and enabling us to keep both pulleys perfectly aligned.

Fig. 9-7. This picture shows the mountings for the pillow block bearings which are hardwood blocks anchored in a cement base. Note belt guard protecting belt drive to motor, at left (photo by Allen Gill, courtesy Worthington Group).

Fig. 9-8. This flexible coupling is essential as it takes up any misalignment between the jackshaft and pump. Make sure jackshaft and pump shaft are aligned as closely as possible or the rubber tire will get very hot from unnecessary flexing. The tire should run cool with proper alignment (courtesy Reliance Electric Co.)

To make sure we had the proper tension on the belts Steve bought a belt tightener gauge. With a half inch depression of one of the three belts there should be five pounds of pressure. Thus, after burning out one set of belts from slippage because they were not tight enough and almost causing a fire from the friction, (which would have spread to the temporary wooden belt guard I had made to protect visitors from the revolving belt) we now have the scientific way of determining proper tension. I mention this, because five pounds of pressure to deflect the belt in its center, between each pulley, seems to be very tight. Once these three Dayco power wedge

Fig. 9-9. This pillow block bearing is mounted so the jackshaft will turn easily. Because of the heavy radial thrust from the belt drive a roller bearing for the pulley end of the shaft is advised rather than ball bearings (courtesy of Reliance Electric Co.).

Fig. 9-10. To make certain that the motor does not skew when tension is put on the belts, Dr. Kleinschmidt made this belt tightener. The ends rest against the pulleys on the jackshaft and motor. Belt tension is increased by tightening the nut which drives the threaded screw out. To rely solely on cranking the motor on its base, would cause it to slip sideways and misalign the belt pulleys.

cog belts (number 3 V X 950) have been run in (24 hours) and then tightened they will last ten years or so with continuous use. Though two of the three belts are rated sufficiently strong to turn "Big Steve" Dr. Kleinschmidt thought it wise to have this coefficient of safety built into the operation. See Figs. 9-8 through 9-10.

Big Steve's pulley is about 5½ inches diameter compared to the 5 and ¾ inches of the one on the jackshaft. "Big Steve's" shaft is about 39 inches from the jackshaft.

Once the installation of the mechanical pieces of equipment was accomplished, came the much more complicated process of wiring the rig to produce power.

Chapter 10

Wiring

Once the actual construction of the physical facilities was completed and the various mechanical components in place (see Fig. 10-1) the next operation was to wire everything up.

Since I was completely dependent on Steve for direction and since by now Rod Bemis was ready and eager to work on the project. I turned to him for his expert help. He is a skillful and competent lineman. Why should I, a rank amateur, take far longer to do it, and not do it as well, when I had experienced help at hand? Rod could follow the schematic drawings. He knew how to work with the electrical conduit which was installed between "Big Steve" and the circuit controls.

For the magnetic motor starter, Steve had been able to pick up an old Allen Bradley starter for $200 (see Fig. 10-2). Because this was the first interconnection on Co-op lines, Vermont Electric's chief engineer, John Bohn wanted to approve Steve's schematic and have an under and over voltage control so that the unit would automatically cut out when line voltage dropped below 115 volts. Should the line voltage drop, line crews would immediately be out investigating the trouble, and he didn't want anyone electrocuted by our feeding juice into the line. To allay his fears, Steve sent a complete schematic layout of the project to him for the Co-op's

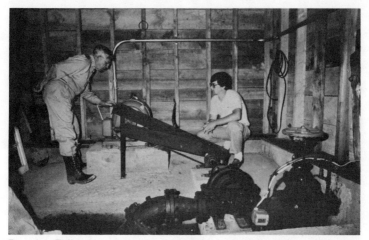

Fig. 10-1. This is how the inside of the powerhouse looks. Author at left. Larry Shafer, a Worthington Engineer—examining the set up. (Photo by Gill).

approval. This procedure should of course, be followed by anyone, contemplating co-generation.

It is a wise procedure also, to have one's installation checked out by a competent engineer before the switch is thrown. By so doing one may save himself lots of grief as well as money if something is amiss. See Figs. 10-3 through 10-5.

Fig. 10-2. This shows the electrical equipment on the wall to the right of the entrance of the penstock. Note first the watt-hour meter, which registers kilowatt hours generated. Note conduit bringing wires from "Big Steve." Underneath the watt-hour meter is the stop-start button. The long oblong box is the magnetic starter for the generator. The smaller box immediately to its right is the starter for the capacitor which is on the sill immediately below the central control box. (Photo by Gill).

Fig. 10-3. The magnetic starter box is open. Note the starter for the capacitor on the floor in the right corner of the building, underneath the central control box. (Photo by Gill).

COMPONENTS AND PROCEDURES

To connect the powerhouse with the house, Rod and Bud, his father, had set two poles and strung two lines of tri-flex #2 wire. Tri-flex is a 3 wire cable which thus gave us 4 wires and 2 neutrals. One wire and one neutral were used to bring electricity from the Co-op to the powerhouse with a side tap to the sugarhouse and the three remaining wires and neutral carried the three phase electricity generated by "Big Steve" back to the house.

To know exactly what was happening (how much current was generated and how it was used) Steve installed a watt-hour meter in the powerhouse which was graduated in 20 kilowatts and then placed three old watt-hour meters, scrounged from the Co-op (which was discarding its old 4 digit meters) one on each phase in the breezeway control panel in the house. When we first generated we were running the Co-op's watt-hour meter which indicated my electrical use, backwards at a great rate. Though this was capital, I knew the Co-op wouldn't like that, so I called up to apprise our manager, Bill Gallagher, of the situation. Very shortly Co-op linemen were down, installing two meters in place of the one, each with a ratchet or detente to prevent its registering backwards.

In the powerhouse itself Steve placed, a fuse box, a relay box (housing 3 relays) a frequency band monitor, and the over

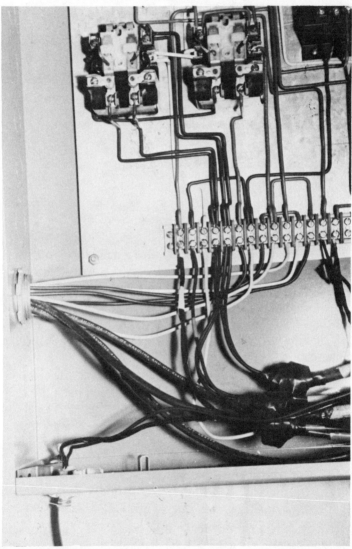

Fig. 10-4. The inside of the central control box looks like this. Its layout is given in detail by the schematic wiring diagrams to follow.

and under voltage control. Then he installed the magnetic starter, a start and stop button, as well as the watt-hour meter referred to above. In the generator circuit, Steve placed a large capacitor (also with a starter) much smaller than the big Allen Bradley magnetic motor starter. This small starter for the capacitor was one Steve had with a burned out coil. Though it was quite old he still was able to obtain a new coil for it.

To wire these various components together so that all the electricity from the three phases of the generator would be funneled into the one house phase, was a job for the master electrician—which Steve was, and more. The following schematic drawings and wiring diagrams give the complete layout. See Figs. 10-6 through 10-8.

DIRECTIONS FOR STARTING THE SYSTEM

Once all the wiring has been checked and water is ready to turn the turbine the following instructions should be followed to start operations.

To start

1. Turn on control power by screwing in the two 15 amp fuses in fuse box. In our case these were the two left fuses the others controlled the lighting circuit in the powerhouse.

2. Close the general disconnect switch on the magnetic starter.

3. Slowly open the six inch gate valve until the turbine comes up to speed.

4. Push starter button. The magnetic starter should close with a bang. Should it hum excessively, push the stop and start buttons in quick successions.

5. If magnetic starter does not close, open the gate valve further.

6. If this is insufficient trouble shooting is in order.

To stop

1. Close gate valve.

2. When turbine slows below generating speed the pressure switch will automatically disconnect the generator and the rig will slow down and stop as valve is closed.

3. Turn off control power by unscrewing the fuses.

Fig. 10-5. When the turbine revs up the motor to generating speed, the pressure switch energizes the stator, and the rotor, turning about 60 rpm faster than the motor speed automatically becomes a generator when the starter button is pushed. When that happens the magnetic switch at the bottom of the starter slams shut with a bang and generation begins.

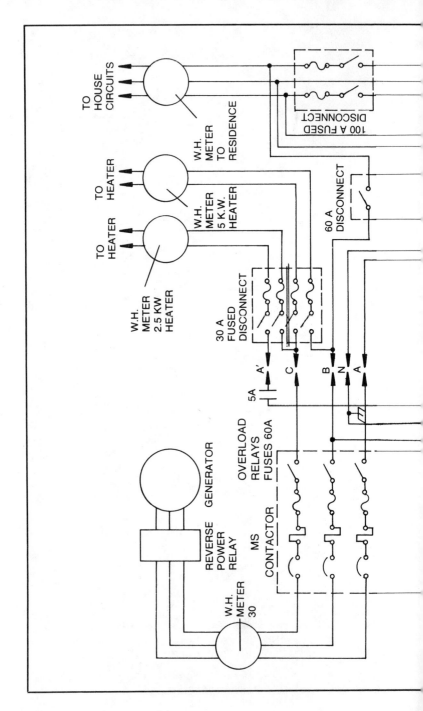

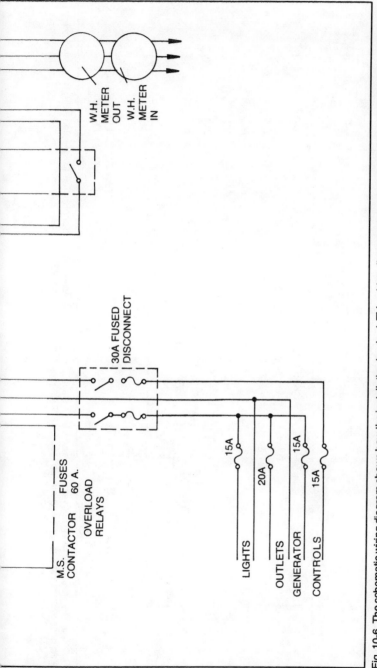

Fig. 10-6. The schematic wiring diagram shows how the installation is wired. This wiring diagram shows how to wire alarm circuit to sound bell and alert household to the system being off line (courtesy R. S. Kleinschmidt).

123

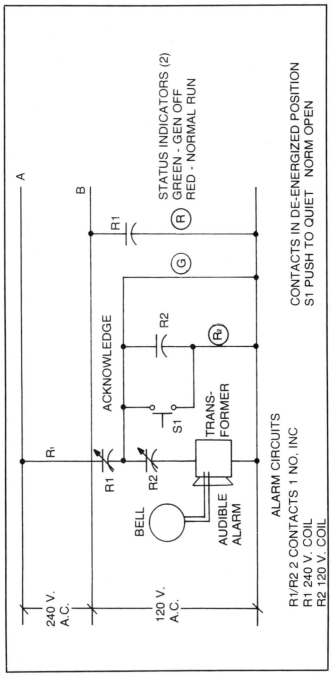

Fig. 10-6. The schematic wiring diagram shows how the installation is wired. This wiring diagram shows how to wire alarm circuit to sound bell and alert household to the system being off line (courtesy R. S. Kleinschmidt) (continued from page 123).

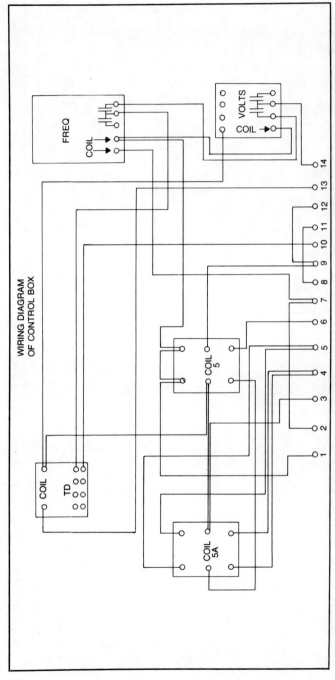

WIRING DIAGRAM
OF CONTROL BOX

Fig. 10-7. The wiring diagram must be followed precisely for this set-up to work. This central control panel in powerhouse is the nerve center of the operation (courtesy of R. S. Kleinschmidt).

125

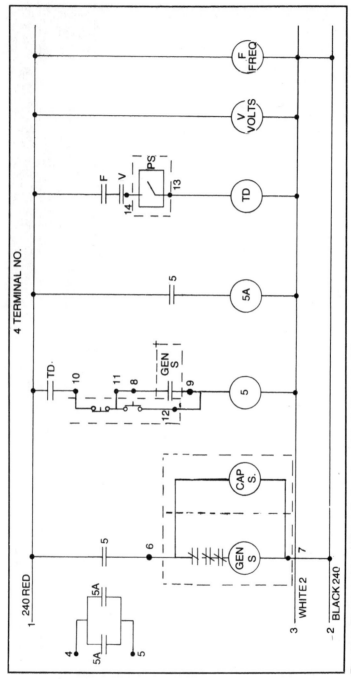

Fig. 10-8. The control box schematic (courtesy of R. S. Kleinschmidt).

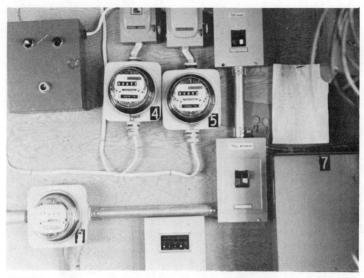

Fig. 10-9. The control panel in the dwelling, located in the breezeway consists of the following: upper left, panel with green and red lights. Green indicates the system is down and red indicates the system is generating. Directly below lights is the watt-hour meter to measure the total kilowatts used in house excluding the kilowatts used for electric heat. This meter includes both electricity drawn from the Co-op, and used as well as the current generated by "Big Steve". Immediately to right of the lights panel are two watt-hour meters. The one on right measures the kilowatts used in the 2½ kW duct heater the other in the 5 kW duct heater. Master switch is on right, below 5 kW duct heater meter. Switch to cut current to powerhouse is directly above it. Immediately to the right of these switches is a magnetic tape recorder, installed by Vermont Electric Co-op to monitor what the generator was doing every 15 minutes on a month long tape. Far right, on wall is the transfer switch for a small 2500 watt auxiliary gasoline generator.

THE ALARM SYSTEM

Should the Co-op line have a temporary interruption of house current this will automatically dump "Big Steve" meaning that the turbine will speed up without load and possibly do damage both to it and the rotor in the motor. Hence, it is essential that an alarm system be wired to alert one to this contingency.

An old fashioned door bell, mounted in the house, with a relay which trips when current no longer is generated, gives the alarm. When this occurs the standard light system used in generating plants works changing the generating light from red meaning current in the wires to green indicating safety.

Fig. 10-10. These meters are mounted on outside house wall. The top meter shows the amount of current drawn from the Co-op. The bottom one gives the total amount of energy returned to the Co-op.

Fig. 10-11. "Bud" Bemis setting an old Vermont Electric Cooperative pole with his backhoe close by my sugar house on right.

There is another value we have discovered to these warning lights. Our cat, Blitzen, loves to sleep in the breeze-way on the shelf next to the hot air inlet from the garage

Fig. 10-12. Rodney Bemis on top of the pole stringing two triflex wires which give one circuit to bring power to the powerhouse and three circuits to bring the three phase electricity back to the house.

Fig. 10-13. The wires are now attached to the poles and Rod climbs back down to tighten the spans from the powerhouse end and connect them into the powerhouse.

furnace. These monitor lights provide him with a very useful night light, which he thoroughly enjoys, as do his owners also. See Figs. 10-9 through 10-13.

Chapter 11

Converting a Forced Hot Air Furnace to Electric

Everyone knows that electric heat is expensive. Vermont's Commissioner of the newly created Public Service Department suggests that there be a special tax on out of state skiers who come to their electrically heated chalets during the cold winter months and push demand for electric power so high that the state's utilities have great difficulty in meeting it. This past December with the mercury plunging to between 25 and 35 degrees below zero in Vermont the state had a new record peak demand. The Vermont Electric Cooperative broke its old record peak at 7 P.M. Christmas day with a peak demand 4.17% over the previous one achieved last year.

Because of this widely held belief about electric heat, it is no wonder that the Department of Energy turned down my application for an "Appropriate Technology Grant" to build my demonstration plant. Such grants were subject to peer review. And my project was turned down on two counts: because I proposed to install the capability of using my surplus electricity to heat my house and because I proposed to have a high head installation.

Everyone knows (at least in Washington) that high heads mean high dams, dangerous to the environment, and dangerous to humans by the constant threat of dam breaks and floods.

The Public Service Board Chairman was right, when at the dedication, he alluded to "my cussedness." I was so

131

incensed at the stupidity of the factotums in DOE that I borrowed the money and determined to show Washington's bureaucrats that all the wisdom did not reside in the capitol and that common folk in the hinterland could make a significant contribution to solving the nation's energy crisis.

I found out that resistance heaters are made in various sizes and they are made to be installed in the duct work of a forced hot air furnace. Thus, for several hundred dollars it was possible to convert forced oil fired hot air to electric heat without adding to the strain on already overburdened utilities. If one lives in the cold country and has a large enough stream and sufficient head to harness it then he can count on selling his surplus electricity to his utility at a good price or if the price that the utility offers is too low he can then substitute his electricity for oil heat.

In 1970 oil sold for less than two dollars a barrel. Then, oil was used to generate 60 percent of New England's electric power. Now, the price is nearly forty dollars a barrel. There is no getting around the fact that oil is convenient, clean, and very expensive. In the present energy emergency over half of Vermont households, have turned to wood. Yet wood has two disadvantages if one does not have his own woodlot. First, it is even more costly than coal. Recently I bought some stove coal for my kitchen range, a Cottage Crawford which graced the kitchen of my wife's childhood home in New Haven, Connecticut. When we came to Vermont over 25 years ago, we brought it along. And how many maple syrup customers have "drooled" over it and offered to pay $500 spot cash for it! I mention this, to give a comparative economic picture of coal, versus wood, and oil. A $100-dollar cord of wood does not give half the heat a ton of stove coal does. And 200 gallons of oil equals the heat value of a ton of coal. In 1981 I paid 119 dollars a ton for stove coal. From prior experience I have learned to burn big coal. Then sift the ashes, and the siftings are the size of chestnut coal which is the usual size many people burn. This "trick" enables me to use the siftings more effectively.

The second disadvantage of wood is that older people and handicapped persons can not lug it or give the fire the constant attention it needs. Hence, to substitute "homemade power" for alternate fuels can make great sense. How much one uses, depends on the economics of interconnection which I shall discuss in a later chapter.

Though combination coal-wood-oil furnaces have made their appearance on the market, they are expensive. The method which I have used is simple, and costs only several hundred dollars.

ELECTRIC DUCT HEATING

When I approached the question of where I would obtain an electric duct heater I first asked my jobber. He had done good reasonable work in the past. His suggestions in this area seemed very reasonable. I sent the "specs" to Steve. He concurred. While one could rig up his own resistance heater such equipment can be dangerous and it is far wiser to buy a ready made unit with all the controls and safety devices. The prices I obtained were 130 dollars for a 5 kilowatt heater and just over 100 dollars for a 2½ kilowatt job. A separate electric thermostat to control this unit will cost in the range of 15 to 20 dollars.

The installation of this unit is easy. All one needs is a pair of offset tin snips, some sheet metal screws, and number 10 or 12 wire. Wire sizes are graduated with the largest size having the smallest number.

The installation of resistance duct heaters does not disturb the oil burner in anyway. It remains as it always has functioned except that now it is relegated to "back-up" status if for any reason one's hydro plant is down. The resistance duct heaters I obtained were manufactured by Emerson Electric's plant in Wytheville, Virginia. I did not go to "Tom-Cat" for the purpose of comparative shopping because Steve thought this was a good price, the unit was just what we needed and was readily available.

WIRING

Wiring for the duct heaters is as follows. The five kilowatt job is on one "leg" of Big Steve. The 2½ kW unit is on a second, with the third phase from Big Steve hooked into the house circuits for normal use. However, the wiring is so arranged that when these duct heaters are not drawing energy the current from their two legs all flows into the house leg. The five kilowatt unit has its own thermostat separate from the oil thermostat. It is wired so that it controls both the resistance heater and the hot air furnace blower.

Our house has a peculiar layout. The dining room-kitchen wing was added in 1946 and has no crawl space underneath. I could not furnish heat to the breezeway and garage from the central furnace when I built that addition in 1973. Hence, I installed a small forced hot air furnace in the garage only to be faced with the first Arab oil embargo before the structure was completed. Because of this second furnace arrangement I placed a 2½ kW unit in this furnace also hooked to its own thermostat in the breezeway.

Later I hitched a second 2½ kW unit on this leg and placed it in the duct which heats the living room. This heater is controlled by the same thermostat which controls the 5 kW one. Thus, with this added capacity the living room is warm even in the coldest weather.

These units as furnished by Emerson Electric have a wiring diagram with an airflow switch which will activate them, once the blower is turned on by the thermostat. Steve's set-up eliminates the need for the air-flow switch which saves something like 20 dollars a unit. When the thermostat turns the heater on it simultaneously turns on the blower.

To accomplish load balance between the three phases of "Big Steve" Dr. Kleinschmidt suggested a capacitor be hooked in. A capacitor is a device which "stores" electricity, thus leveling out the flow and protects against sudden surges of current. It is of value not only in keeping the legs of the generator in balance but also in the event that lightning strikes the line to help protect the generator's field. While the cost of this capacitor seemed high (440 dollars) it is worth-while and indeed quite essential to have.

GENERATING WITHOUT ONE'S UTILITY

Last year Vermont had no big winter storms. The year before we were without power for 40 hours. Some Co-op members were without power for 60 hours.

Though the past two winters have been mostly snowless, normal snowfall is 120 inches annually. In many years it exceeds the average. When heavy wet snow coats the lines and makes them the size of hawsers something has to give.

When the Rural Electric Administration was formed by the far sighted imagination of Franklin Roosevelt to bring electricity to rural areas, my home first received electric service in 1938. Rural electric lines suffer from storm damage even more than city systems. To keep costs down those rural electric pioneers followed Euclid's axiom; "A straight line is the shortest distance between two points." Instead of following cowpath roads, twisting and turning about the hills, the REA lines were built straight across country, up hill and down dale, across mountains, through forests, fording streams, traversing terrain very hostile to the intrusion of such new fangled gadgets as power lines.

In those days, there were but two customers per mile of line. No investor owned utility could survive with such a scarcity of customers. Even today, Vermont Electric Co-op has but six customers per mile of line, compared to the largest city in the state, Burlington's 130.

With such rugged terrain it is axiomatic that ice storms bring outages though it is surprising in reality how few outtages there are. Nonetheless, when they occur we are without power. For this reason, ten years ago, I invested in a small 2500 watt auxiliary gasoline generator. With a transfer switch I can easily disconnect from the Co-op lines start the generator and have enough power for minimal needs.

To excite "Big Steve's field with this auxiliary generator is now possible since all the electricity he generates will be used up. Not being connected with the Co-op line to take the surplus power, it is essential that all the current generated be completely used, else it will build up and burn out the generator, or other components of the system.

Chapter 12

Interconnecting
with One's Utility

Federal law or specifically the Public Utilities Regulatory Policy Act (PURPA) requires that utilities buy power generated by small producers from wind, solar, hydro, biomass, geo-thermal, all manner of co-generation available. Naturally, such power must be compatible with the utilities' 60 Hz current so that it can be integrated into the utility's system without difficulty. The federal law does not specify the exact price a utility must pay. It merely says the price must be "reasonable," and that it should be equal to the cost of the last unit of fossil fuel power the utility purchases so as to encourage others to co-generate.

AUTOMATIC SYNCHRONIZATION

The technique of using an induction mill motor as a generator enables one to produce 60 cycle current automatically. When the field of an induction motor is excited by 60 cycle current that frequency is induced when the rotor turns in the magnetic field of the stator. Because of this one does not need to go through the costly process of an inverter to change dc into ac or other more costly and cumbersome devices to regulate the speed of the generator.

If one does not have a utility with which to interconnect, or if one has a small stream with a limited head it might be well to investigate the dc to battery route. Bear in mind however that a plant generating only one kilowatt will turn out 720 kilowatt hours a month which is above the average for a normal household which uses 500 kWhs a month. To interconnect with one or two kilowatts is certainly feasible and practical. Two kW will mean 1440 k WHs a month. One might well be paid for this surplus electricity as wasting it, if a utility's lines are available.

If, on the other hand, one has a brook or stream with larger flow and sufficient head to generate more power, he would be unwise not to utilize it to the fullest if he is going to the expense to build his own power plant. Bear in mind that price figures quoted by various generator-turbine manufacturers, do not reflect the total cost of a system.

The electrical components for my system cost only several thousand dollars. The dam and penstock cost about 12 thousand dollars or roughly two thirds of the entire cost of the project. The powerhouse itself, using salvaged boards from the dam forms to sheathe it, with clapboards and roofing cost something over one thousand dollars even though it is but 12 × 12 feet. See Figs. 12-1 and 12-2.

Some years ago the James Leffel Co. of Springfield, Ohio turned out a 10 kW Hoppes unit which sold for about ten thousand dollars. This unit price did not count the cost of penstock and dam or the cost of transmitting the power from powerhouse to residence let alone the cost of building into the system the capacity of electric heat. Such a cost today is far greater. Should anyone desire to pursue this further he can either write the Leffel Company in Springfield, Ohio, or the Cumberland General Store in Crossville, Tennessee which advertises these Hoppes self-contained units in its catalog.

Further if there is no room beneath the bottom of the intake the pipe will suck all manner of silt and gravel into it which in turn will damage the turbine.

As for "oversized equipment," the two components in my system are the induction mill motor and the pump-turbine. These can be purchased off the shelf and hence far less expensively than a custom built job. They are no more expensive than smaller units which have the disadvantage of not generating enough electricity so that one may sell his surplus.

Fig. 12-1. Powerhouse with spillway cascading down to the brook.

An ordinary household has peak demands of something like 15 kilowatts. Unless one can produce at least that much electricity he either must go the battery bank route or else interconnect with a large utility in order to provide for peak demands. Our water heater is a 90 gallon tank which draws 5200 watts. So does the clothes dryer. Add the refrigerator, freezer, electric stove, TV and lights and unless you have that much capacity you must obtain it from batteries, your utility, or suffer a brown-out.

Suppose for instance, one builds a 10 kW system such as I have. Normally on average, I use 1½ kilowatts an hour. Since there are 720 hours in a month, that means my average load is about 1050 kWhs a month. Yet, if I generate continuously, 10 kW an hour times 720 hours a month, would give me 7200 kilowatt hours a month.

When I am using such a small amount of the electricity I can produce for my normal needs (without heat of course) it would be foolish to throttle back the generator to just produce what was needed at the moment. There would be times I needed more and couldn't produce it. But more importantly, unless I did throttle back the production there would be on average 6½ times the energy I need with no place for it to go. Such an overload would quickly burn up the system. Hence, it becomes imperative for the system's well being, to funnel that surplus power back to the utility. Doing that makes the small hydro system healthy. More than that it is true conservation as well as providing income to help amortize the cost of the installation.

Many years ago, when I was a small boy, I heard an older cousin explain how the electrified railroads used the principle

Fig. 12-2. Here are some visitors to the dam in the winter.

of the induction motor as a generator in saving energy. When the train was going down a steep grade in the Cascades, or Rockies, the engineer would pull a switch in the cab and instead of having to burn out brake shoes with friction to dissipate the energy generated by the grade, the weight of the train turned the motors and they became generators thus putting back into the lines some of the energy consumed on the upward pull.

THE ECONOMIC ADVANTAGES OF CO-GENERATION

If one does build a small hydroelectric unit and can sell his surplus electricity to his utility, he stands to gain significantly from the sale. It also makes one feel he is contributing to help solve the nation's energy emergency. The value of such co-generated energy can only go one way—up. As time goes on, such a plant will continue to produce revenue. The question to be faced by any co-generator is: how much should the utility pay for co-generated power?

To answer this question requires an understanding of how utilities purchase power. The cost of electricity to a utility is divided into two parts: a cost for capacity and a charge for the energy. Presently, capacity charges run something like $60 a kilowatt a year. That means, when a non-generating utility pays this fee, the generating utility agrees to make that power available whenever the other utility calls on it. Second, there is the charge for the actual energy delivered. Naturally a utility hooked into the utility grid (or in the case of the Vermont Electric Cooperative the New England Power Pool) there are several sources of power: hydro, nuclear, coal, oil, and natural gas. Over all, the capacity charge that Vermont Electric Co-op has had to pay has been 7 mills, and the energy cost per kilowatt hour, 20 mills. That these rates are escalating as fast as the cost of Arab Oil is apparent.

Inasmuch as the Public Utilities Regulatory Policy Act mandated that utilities purchase such excess power as I produce, I asked that the Vermont Public Service Board give me opportunity to speak at its public hearing to set such rates.

Accordingly, I submitted written testimony, and then spoke in person at the hearing.

Following is my written testimony:

In December 1978, Rural Electric Administration Robert W. Feragen wrote all Rural Electric Cooperatives, urging that they pioneer with all kinds of co-generation: biomass, wind, solar, low-head hydro. Because of this national policy, and because I had long been an advocate of using Vermont's swift flowing streams, now neglected, but once the cause of its pre-eminence in the 19th century, I built my own small, 10 kW hydroelectric facility.

I should like to address my comments to the questions: What is fair? What will encourage the development of similar co-generation projects to use Vermont's renewable resources for electric power?

Dr. R. Stevens Kleinschmidt DSc Harvard, one of the leading hydroelectric engineers in New England worked with me on this project, designing a totally new, innovative method for harnessing such small streams as I have. With Steve Kleinschmidt's active support, using his theories, I have built, and put to the empirical test that which he thought would work from theory. It works better than we dreamed.

We were turned down by "Appropriate Technology" of DOE, probably because we have a "high head" installation, and because we use the surplus "juice" to heat our house. This program was subject to peer review. I assume we were turned down because anyone knows that electric heat is wasteful, and two, that high heads, in this case, 225 feet, mean enormous dams. Both assumptions are false.

Because Dr. Kleinschmidt was so supportive, I determined to build the project on my own, borrowing money, and finishing it without government help. I spent about $17,500. Though this is c. $1750/kW of installed capacity, it is not as expensive as some. Of course, my own labor is not included, which would bring its cost higher. But my location was not ideal, requiring 2700 feet of 6 inch pvc pipe to obtain 225 feet of head. The 4½ foot concrete dam, plus laying the more than half mile of pipe through the woods, was responsible for over two thirds of the cost.

Included in this cost is the expense of converting my forced hot air oil furnace, to also use my own electricity to heat the house.

This installation is unique for two reasons:

1. Dr. Kleinschmidt believed a centrifugal pump, run backwards would serve equally well as a turbine. We found practically no loss in efficiency vis a' vis a Pelton wheel. Many said no: a pump is a pump. But we have proved Dr. Kleinschmidt's theory correct by the empirical test. We lose practically no efficiency, and had far less cost with a pump from "off the shelf" as compared with a custom built turbine.

2. From his theoretical knowledge of electricity he correctly saw that an old induction mill motor, in this case, a 20 horse for which he paid $183 turned 60 rpm faster than the operating speed of 1740 rpm, with its field excited by 60 Hz, being an induction motor, would produce induced current at exactly 60 cycles, and hence completely synchronous with the utility, thus allowing interconnection. One cfs a second of water at 225 feet of head turns out 10 kilowatts.

This we have done, and demonstrated, much to Dr. Kleinschmidt's and my satisfaction. Indeed Governor Snelling stopped by to see this innovative rig as he is a graduate of Lehigh and interested in engineering matters.

In building this project, I had in mind the old Chinese Proverb, one picture is worth a thousand words. I am Town Energy Coordinator (Town of Halifax). For four years I have tried to obtain funds for feasibility studies of the North River in town. May's Mill, and the F.H. Stone mill sites offer falls of c. 100 feet, which can be harnessed with equally small dams as mine, and will turn out 3½ million or so kilowatt hours of electricity a year, according to Dr. Kleinschmidt. The Army Corps of Engineers estimate more. Suffice to say, the town of Halifax, because of my project, is enthusiastic about this idea, and at last we have obtained a 90-10 feasibility loan from the Department of Energy. Engineering studies are now in progress for a Halifax Municipal Hydroelectric facility.

In passing, I must mention the invaluable help John White of the State Energy Office gave me in obtaining DOE's cooperation. Further, my backhoe man, Howard Bemis, is also President of the Village Electric of Jacksonville, Vermont. Jacksonville has a splendid opportunity to develop hydropower from Gates and Jacksonville Ponds, covering 56 acres, with a head of well over 100 feet in a very short linear distance. Howard Bemis' son, Rodney lineman for the Village Electric, is also a Selectman, Town of Halifax. He worked with me on my project and became very enthused about it. Indeed he helped install the gage station on the North River as a result and it looks exceedingly favorable that my prototype project will spark several far more significant developments in the area.

I pointed out in my letter of Sept. 4, China has 70,000 small hydroelectric installations, averaging but 42 kWs each, but turning out an aggregate of approximately 3,000,000 kilowatts. (Bulletin of the Atomic Scientists, Feb. '77)

While one 10 kilowatt project is in and of itself meaningless, the power of example is great. I have a contract with TAB Books to write a book, How To Build One's Own Hydro. With proper guidance, this technology which I have outlined can help not only Vermont, but any area of the nation where there are small fast flowing streams to beat the energy emergency. In the East, the entire Appalachian chain; in the West, the Sierras, the Rockies, the Cascade mountains, as well as the Piedmont, present unparalleled opportunities for using renewable, non-polluting energy sources such as this, Co-generation is a viable alternative to oil and nuclear power.

In co-generation projects such as mine, utilities do not have to make huge capital investments for new generating equipment, particularly for peaking power.

Last summer, Vermont Electric Co-op tried to have me sign a contract to sell power to it for 2c a kilowatt hour. I refused. I said I would rather give it any surplus than accept such a figure.

The economics are straightforward. By using resistance heaters I have converted, very simply, my forced hot air furnace to electric with oil as a backup. Each kWh has just over 3400 BTUs, which is completely recoverable at 100 percent efficiency. Net efficiency for a gallon of oil is about 90,000 BTUs. Thus, electricity even at 3c a kWh is cheaper for me to burn for fuel, than to sell to the Co-op. At 4c a kWh, with oil at $1.05 (sic!) a gallon, it would be economically feasible to sell the surplus "juice" to the Co-op.

The contract VEC preferred me had me paying the full retail rate for the electricity I buy from the Co-op, with its obtaining my power for 2c. In other words, they want their cake and to eat it to. It is heads I win, tails you lose. I have checked the operation of the meters—there are seven in all, so that we can monitor exactly how the system works. For instance the timed hot water heater is a 90 gallon tank, which burns 5200 watts. If I have my two freezers and refrigerator on, they, without the water heater, plus 7½ kWs of resistance heating take up nearly my entire output. However, when we run the clothes or dishwasher, if I disconnect the 5 kW duct heater, I find that I do not draw any juice from the Co-op.

It is very feasible for me to turn back my entire surplus, or nearly all, to the Co-op during peaking hours, from 4 to 10 P.M. Since my average use is c. 1050 kWhs monthly, that means I generate on average about 6½ times my needs, without heat. Thus, it is apparent, such a system of co-generation, can help utilities with peaking power requirements if the monetary incentive is there.

VEC has not paid anything toward the capital costs of this project. Such installations relieve it, and similar utilities of large capital burdens. That ought to be worth a lot to them.

Some point out that hydro is not available all the year. True, and particularly so this past year. With less than average rainfall, and no snow run-off, we have had a very bad experience. But bear in mind, VEC's summer load peak is c. 11 MW whereas in winter it rises to 28½ MW. Such hydro as mine is generally available when the Co-op faces its peak power needs.

I ask you to look at New Hampshire's rates for co-generation and the comment the New Hampshire Cooperative News, August 1980, made, to which I referred in my earlier letter to you.

If such a rate (7¢ /kWh) seems too high, then a compromise might be worked out on these lines: the Co-op has filed for a 9¢ base winter rate. Why should not the Co-op pay me the same rate, particularly during the daily peak, as it charges me? At other hours, the rate could be less, once the kWhs I sell equal what I must buy.

As I understand it, the purpose of PURPA is to fix these rates for co-generation so as to encourage its development. Last May, at the Northeast Association of Rural Electric Co-ops, in West Lebanon, New Hampshire, Vermont Electric's Chief Engineer reported that the Co-op would have to charge 12¢ for the power it expects from the North Hartland hydroelectric project. Here, the dam is already in place, having been built by the Army Corps of Engineers in 1961.

To illustrate the situation further, I was generating splendidly the other day when all of a sudden, my magnetic starter blew up. The old coil was 220 volt, not 240. It could not stand the added pressure. I called Keene, ordered a new coil, $80 which will take 4 weeks to be made and delivered. Additionally, I learned from Burlington Electric Dept. of a splendid coil winder in that city, so I shipped the old coil to him, hoping I can be back in business quickly.

I am simply incensed at the suggested price of 2¢ a kWh. The Co-op's annual reports for the past two years aver that 54¢ of each dollar goes to the cost of purchased power. Since the base is now about 6¢ retail, that means, more than 3¢ per kWh would equal present costs. If proposed tariffs go into effect, with a base of 9¢, that would mean a significantly higher figure.

I therefore urge the PSB to consider all these factors: the value of encouragement of additional energy resources, the encouragement of Yankee ingenuity and self-reliance, and fixing a figure as PURPA proposes, that will encourage co-generation, a figure equal to the equivalent of the last increment of cost of fossil fuel (oil) generated power, that such co-generation replaces.

Respectfully submitted,
J. George Butler

As this is written there has been no determination by the Public Service Board of the rates it intends to fix. I elaborate this matter in detail, as others following the same route as I will have to follow the same process. One must have rates fixed, not by the self interest of a utility, but by an impartial arbitrator who can see the whole matter in its broadest perspective.

While it is true that in the winter I can use all the power I generate, come spring, with normal spring run-off, there will be significant power to sell. Those living in warmer climates will have surplus power to sell the entire fall and winter seasons as well as spring.

Chapter 13

Murphy's Law

"Nothing is as easy as it looks.
Everything takes longer than you expect.
And if anything can go wrong, it will,
At the worst possible moment."

I believe in Murphy's Law! Several years ago, I became a believer. Now, with the empirical evidence amassed in building and dealing with my hydro, any lingering doubts and skepticism have vanished. Does one scoff at such superstition? Consider the evidence. Three years ago we were in a neighboring town and saw some attractive coffee mugs with Murphy's Law inscribed on them.

"Nice little presents," my wife opined. I concurred. So we bought half a dozen, despite the jocular warnings of the proprietor of the shop. Barely had we pulled into the dooryard when the radiator of the car burst, sending a geyser of steam shooting into the air.

"Lucky," I said, "that this didn't happen when we were in Greenfield."

"Lucky?" questioned June. "We don't need that kind of luck, having this happen." June then opened the door to get out of the car. The bag holding the cups broke. All six of them smashed on the ground. Two strikes for Murphy!

We went into the house for a late lunch, after cleaning up the pieces of our erstwhile presents. Once lunch was over, Murphy struck again. June tried to start the clothes dryer. It broke. I climbed into the cramped quarters behind it and the washer, and tried to fix it. My glasses caught, fell off, and they broke!

The next day I was scheduled to go up state, almost to the Canadian border for a board meeting of the Vermont Electric Cooperative. The garage couldn't get a new radiator so my friend soldered the old one. We then crossed our fingers and our toes, said ten "Hail Marys" and hoped.

Whether it was the crossed fingers or toes, or the benign intervention of St. Mary I do not know. One of them put the hex on Murphy—I got home safely without mishap!

But Murphy wasn't done. I finally obtained a new radiator. Have you ever priced a new one recently? Then the battery went dead. Next, the entire electrical system went. We had to trace every electrical circuit on the car. Finally we found the short circuit. The end result? Several hundred dollars in garage bills, a new alternator, and the same old car! This is a true story, the plain, unvarnished truth.

But one may still aver it was coincidence? In high fallutin language, nothing more than the fortuitous concatenation of events, without any malign mischief from Mr. Murphy? Well, maybe. I leaned to this latter version until we tested his law further.

A year ago, we went back to the same shop, and replaced our "treasured Murphy Mugs." We got them home safely. But I wish we had never seen the pesky things. Consider what has happened to my hydro project. I now aver on a stack of Holy Writ: Murphy is a malign malingerer, a Mephistophelian metaphysician, who diabolically dreams up evil to befall the unwary. His ability to derail a project is beyond belief.

Let's look at the record. Murphy first made himself felt with the boys I had working for me in building the dam. They lost their knapsack and bank book while riding home from work on their motorcycle. Murphy then persuaded them to lose every tool they touched: peevees, shovels, pry bars, picks, hammers, lopping shears. Somehow he mysteriously hid them from prying eyes. The lopping shears disappeared permanently. I can only surmise they must lie buried among tons of rock and debris pushed on the penstock bed by the bulldozer.

In taking my "family heirloom" cement mixer up to the dam on the trailer, Murphy made the mixer fall off, breaking its handle. Yet these were merely omens of things to come. Any impartial observer, on the basis of the objective evidence, who properly evaluates the trials and tribulations of my hydro must conclude: Murphy's Law has had a great influence on the course of events.

Take Murphy's dictum: "Everything takes longer than you expect." I had expected to be on line by the fall of 1979. I wasn't. The dam was done. The powerhouse was built and resplendent in its newly stained clapboards. The two second hand poles were set and the transmission wires strung. What was lacking was but the electrical equipment for the powerhouse. Steve had ordered the stuff but it hadn't come. The delay of a month had serious consequences, which of course, could have been foretold by anyone familiar with Murphy. This was the winter Vermont had no snow. Ski operators cried. Many ancillary businesses went bankrupt. Because there was no snow blanket, the ground froze to record levels.

Before the freeze in October, John Carnahan and I had removed the stop from the mouth of the funnel of the penstock. Water had caused the boards to swell and it was a water-tight stop. The plywood stop I slid into the slots to hold it was not so tight and water seeped around it. And that water froze solidly. Ice didn't finally thaw from the penstock until Easter Sunday 1980. Whether that date was symbolic or not, I do not know. At any rate, it was a glorious resurrection for my spirits. I telephoned Steve exultantly. "We're generating," I cried.

Naturally, any new plant must get the bugs worked out. We set the dedication ceremony for May 9, adequate time we thought to have everything running as it should. Murphy saw to it that more bugs developed. The three drive belts transmitting the mechanical power from the pump-turbine to the motor-generator started to slip. When I came by in the evening to inspect the plant, I once again found the house filled with smoke. This time there was no elation. Friction had worn off the cogs of the cog belts and ruined them. Fortunately however, the wooden belt guard I had made until the blacksmith could fashion a permanent metal one was only charred. It could have caught fire and then the whole powerhouse could have burned down. With that warning, I pulled the temporary wooden guard off. If it were a choice between the Occupational Safety and Health Administration rules, or the powerhouse's standing intact, I opted for the latter. I would keep visitors out until I had the permanent guard in place.

To prevent such a situation in the future, Steve bought a belt tightening gauge, a small spring loaded pencil type contraption, which would measure the pressure required to deflect the belts a half inch at the midway point between the pulleys of the pump and motor. According to Dayco V belt cog pulleys, 5 pounds is the proper tension. Then Steve fashioned a belt tightening device so that the motor pulley would stay plumb with the pump pulley as the motor was being moved to tighten the belt. Two hardwood blocks, (shaped to fit against the curvature of the pulleys, connected by telescoping rod, adjustable by a hex nut) would push the motor pulley back into its proper alignment when the sliding base mount of the motor was cranked to increase tension. Unless some such device is used it is impossible to get the belts tight enough without having the motor pulley become misaligned. Once the belts have undergone their original stretching, they will last for ten years, without a great deal more stretching.

Then there were minor matters. For years I have used a three wire electric fence to keep all manner of miscreants out of my acre garden. By stretching the first wire six inches above ground, the next fifteen inches, and the last, two feet, it is possible to keep all animals from deer to woodchuck, raccoon, porcupine, rabbits and foxes from enjoying the fruits of my labor. This year, when I turned on the electric fence charger, I immediately upset the frequency band monitor, and the system went "down." Finally I found out: instead of widening the band on the monitor, I simply turned the plug around on the fence charger and the trouble was over.

Then there was the matter of the CBS presentation of my project. Charles Kuralt, had promised to film the hydro for his show. He sent Charles Osgood and a film crew, Bill Moren producer, Bert and Herbie, sound and camera men respectively, and they spent two days filming everything under the sun. Since WCAX-TV, Burlington was going to cover the actual dedication, Charlie left explicit directions: he wanted WCAX, the CBS affiliate in Vermont, to get a picture of the Whitingham High School band playing the Star Spangled Banner at the opening of the dedicatory exercises. But Murphy fixed that. The girl from WCAX had a flat tire, and arrived late. The band had packed up and gone home! The reporter was so concerned that she feared her job was on the line, because Charles had been so explicit that that was what he wanted!

Added to that mishap, the day was blustery, rain squalls, raw and chill, more like March, than the month of flowers. But it was a gala affair nonetheless. Senator Patrick Leahy and his wife were present. Senator Robert Stafford sent a warm letter, expressing his regrets that he could not be here due to a previous commitment. The Chairman of the State Energy Office spoke. The Chairman of the State's Public Service Board proclaimed it a textbook example of what could be done with renewable resources. And Bill Gallagher the Executive Manager of the Vermont Electric Co-op spoke of the value of this kind of co-generation and threw the ceremonial "first switch," to bring the unit on line.

But there was no Governor. I had not invited him. Several years previously I had written him. He had not acknowledged my letter, nor answered my questions. I had even said I had voted for him that year too! Hence, I had concluded the Governor was not interested. But again, Murphy had given me a bum steer. The Governor was interested. He felt hurt that everyone else in Montpelier had been invited, but not he.

Last fall, while campaigning in Brattleboro for re-election, he spoke with my friend on the Brattleboro Reformer, Bruce Simonds, who had covered the story of the dedication. When the Governor expressed his disappointment to him, Bruce, with the prescience given to competent newsmen said: "George told me to invite you now."

So as soon as that luncheon meeting was over, Bruce was on the phone: "George," he said, "the Governor is on his way to see your hydro!" He told me the story.

I said: "Gee, thanks," and had barely time to change my work clothes when the big black Lincoln limousine bearing Vermont 1 plates slid into the dooryard. Undoubtedly Murphy was to blame for my faux pas.

Whether it was that the Governor was "getting even" I do not know. At any rate last December (1980) a conference was held in Montpelier on Natural Resources. I was unable to attend but read the transcript of the meetings. I was aghast to read: the Agency for Environmental Conservation was opposed to "backyard hydro." I immediately wrote both the State Commissioner, and the Governor asking: 1. If it were true that they were opposed to "backyard hydro" and 2. If they were opposed to baseload coal fired plants?

The Environmental Commissioner wrote a very "balanced" reply, the sum and substance of which was: game fish and sportsmen's concerns, under the guise of protecting the environment were more important than the environmental damage "backyard hydro" would do to the free flowing streams of the state. Such hydro, in his view, could contribute but marginally to the state's energy resources. And the Governor didn't bother to respond to either of my two letters, I stopped by his office, after writing the first letter and attempted to see him. He was busy. After the second letter his secretary merely referred me to the Chairman of the Public Service Board. I had already given to the General Counsel of the Public Service Board the Bulletin of the Atomic Scientists with its fascinating article: "China's Intermediate Technology," in the Feb. 1977 issue, which was a classic illustration of Frank Schumacher's thesis: "Small is Beautiful."

To return to the dedication: it was a gala affair withal. The day afterwards however, I noticed the disc of the watt-hour meter in the powerhouse was barely turning. The pump didn't sound right. I shut the water down with the gate valve. Such a valve is imperative so that when opening or closing the valve the flow will be changed very slowly. An immediate shut-off would result in the water causing the pipe to squirm and break loose, and rupturing given the pressure from 225 feet of head at the powerhouse.

The pump literally ground to a halt, emitting a final hrrump as it came to rest. Taking the head off the pump, I found the pump's vanes full of debris, sticks, stones, all manner of stream matter that had gotten into the penstock when we were placing the hardware cloth in front of the trash rack.

At least it didn't happen at the "worst possible time," I thought. But Murphy's malevolence was not finished yet. By the end of May we were out of water just when in a normal year the spring run-off would be at its height. It was incredible, yet understandable when one considers the drought afflicting vast sections of the country this past year. I had simply chosen the worst possible year to build my hydro. Vermont had less snow last year than any year on record. I had rejoiced that I hadn't had to have a bulldozer break out my sugaring roads in the woods. There was no snow to move. But now, I was not so glad. The streams in Vermont, as elsewhere, subsided quickly. The summer of 1980 saw the drought worsen. The statistical table for the past fifteen years given me by a friend in nearby Heath, Massachusetts which he had from keeping precipitation data for the Massachusetts Department of Natural Resources shows a deficit of more than 12" below normal. While it is true that March had 8 inches precipitation last year it was in the form of rain which caused immediate high water water and was quickly gong. Had such precipitation been the usual snow the run-off would have been far more gradual, lasting at least until the end of June.

Last summer the drought continued with a total rainfall for June, July, and August of 6.83 inches. Vermont's Department of Water Resources gives the 25 year average rainfall for these months, from 1948 to 1973, as 12.02 inches, nearly twice as much. As a result, gardens failed, springs and wells ran dry, and so did my brook. I hadn't the prescience when I measured my brook flow that January day two years ago, to realize what was adequate flow then might not be in a dry year. I guess Murphy is responsible for this fix.

As a matter of fact the entire northeast as well as the mid-section of the country is suffering from what must be called "Murphy's drought." Meteorologists from the Travellers' Weather Service in Hartford, Connecticut have records going back 135 years, far longer than those of the U.S. Weather Service. They report that the two months, December 1980 and January 1981 were the two driest consecutive months in the entire history of the Hartford weather station. New York City has declared a water emergency with its reservoirs less than 30 percent full and New Jersey is in far worse shape. Indeed New York was supplying northern New Jersey communities with water from fire hoses laid through the Holland Tunnel until its own water situation became desperate. Stamford, Greenwich, and Manchester, Connecticut are either out of water or with but a few days' supply left.

The New Haven Journal-Courier for January 1, 1981 had a feature story: "State Climate Second Driest On Record." It quoted Roland Laro, Bradley International Airport's meteorologist (Hartford's): " . . . the signs of drought were evident as early as last January—when the lack of precipitation broke a monthly record, making it the second driest January since 1904. The following month the dry conditions worsened, making it the driest February ever.

"And Laro added that the outlook for the new year wasn't much better. The National Weather Service in November put out a winter outlook for the northeast that called for colder and drier than normal." He said. "So far, I would say, they are on the money."

Connecticut's precipitation for 1980 was 12 inches below normal, just about the same figure as for us. My spring, though not failing completely, slowed to a trickle. Normally it flows a full ¾ inch pipe, enough to water my garden all summer long. Now, when ground water levels should be completely replenished, it is still flowing at a snail's pace. Usually by the end of January, my ice fountain is much larger than today.

Even the mighty Mississippi River has been affected. Barge traffic from Cairo, Illinois to Baton Rouge, Louisiana is so hampered by groundings from low water that the Army Engineers are spending $100,000 a day in desperate efforts to keep a nine foot channel open.

But drought is not the last disaster visited on us by Murphy. Last August we had a freak thunderstorm. There was more lightning damage, according to local electricians than they had ever seen before. You guessed it: Murphy's Law held true. We were struck, in spite of lightning arrestors on both triflex wires from the powerhouse to our dwelling. The last Sunday in August we heard a sharp report: "Big Steve" had been hit, and he was mortally wounded. His stator was completely burned out.

Fortunately there was a good motor coil winding shop in Keene, New Hampshire, about 45 miles away. I took "Big Steve" apart and saw the massive damage. I enlisted Rod's help to get the stator on my dolly and with a struggle got the stator into the back of the station wagon.

In a week, I had the stator back $255 poorer to be sure, but glad to have it in time for the fall rains. Unfortunately the fall rains did not come. Every storm to hit the Atlantic Seaboard either went out to sea below us in the mid-Atlantic region or hugged the coast and failed to reach inland to Vermont.

Finally, with trees dormant in November, the stream came up, and we began to generate. I thought I was done with Murphy! I wasn't. The next difficulty came as a result of my ignorance. After all I had never built or operated a hydro plant before. Those who emulate me, take heed.

In the spring, when on one of my daily inspection trips to the dam, I found some of the meshes of the quarter inch hardware cloth which I had put over the trash rack's bars had caught various forms of aquatic life: very small minnows and mollusks. To remedy this, I had immediately put window screening over the hardware cloth. Things went along just fine until leaf season in the fall. Then the screen wire clogged with fallen leaves. To help this, I placed a cedar pole five feet out from the trash rack and ran inch mesh poultry wire to either side of the trash rack. This gave something like ten times the area for collecting leaves and let the hydro run fairly well during the autumn season.

When winter set in the window screening posed another problem. Its fine mesh caught slush ice and again stopped the flow of water. To fix this, I laboriously cut the screen wire off. Next spring when all the ice is gone I will replace the screen wire. This time I will mount it on its own frame, so that it can be removed once the spawning season is over.

As alluded to in my testimony before the Public Service Board, Murphy's Law held true once again, just before Christmas. The old magnetic starter Steve had obtained for $200 was a bargain, but it was so old, it was built for old style voltage of 110-220 volts, rather than today's higher, 120/240 volts. And again, the powerhouse filled with smoke, the smoke of burning insulation as the stater's coil burned out. My coil winder in Keene did not have such a coil in stock. He would have to order it from the factory. It would take at least a month.

I called Steve. He had heard tell of an excellent coil winder in Burlington. He gave me the name of a friend at the Burlington Electric Department who could give me the name. I called him. Then I called the coil winder: Henry Metevier. I've never seen him, yet because he knew this was an emergency, he got that coil back to me in less than a week, counting time for parcel post one way, and UPS the other. Henry is that wonderful kind of small business man: competent and skilled not only in the art of coil winding, but also so sensitive to the needs of his customers. Henry, when there is a rush job, will work 14 hours a day to get the work done. What a refreshing experience to find such competence and concern in today's world.

But Henry's efforts were in vain. Christmas day was the coldest Christmas I've ever seen, −25 degrees. With very little snow cover, once again frost penetrated the ground deeply. Officials at Central Vermont Public Service Corporation in Rutland found the frost to be 5 feet deep. With such cold that hung on for weeks the ground water froze. The stream, deprived of its normal rainfall and snow cover simply dried up. When finally it did start to run, it ran so gradually that once again the penstock froze. How agonizing it was to watch the pump-turbine gradually slow down, then cease to turn, and finally to bind up tight with ice. But this year, unlike last, we had an extended thaw after the first part of February. The ice went out of the brook and the pipe began to drip in the powerhouse. Then I heard another drip. I looked closely. Murphy had done it again! The big six inch gate valve was ruined—cracked all along the bottom casting. I took it to Percy, my ageless blacksmith. But Percy gave me the bad news: one can't weld cast iron and make it stick. "The first bit of strain, and it will pop open again," he said. The iron granulates from the heat of welding.

So I was up a tree, I needed a new, second hand gate valve. I priced one in Lebanon, New Hampshire. New, the cost was $2,000! Frantically I pursued all leads. One man, the chief tool and die maker for the Ensign Bickford Company, in Simsbury, Connecticut stopped by, Washington's Birthday (new style) to see this "fabulous" rig he had seen on TV. He'd missed my name. But he came anyway—and he found me. I told him my problem.

"We make all our own machinery in Simsbury," he said. "Let me look around the plant, maybe I can find a used one."

"Good," I replied. "And if you can't find one at the company, could you call the junk yards around Hartford? This is a standard valve used in factory sprinkler systems, and second hand ones ought to be plentiful."

Next morning, Don called me. I had told him to call collect. He didn't. All he could find was a 4″ one, he said. And he had checked half a dozen junk yards without success.

So that path shut down. But when I was at Percy's blacksmith shop, another customer was there, from Rowe Massachusetts.

He told me: "Call Gene Gates. He knows every junk yard and second hand machinery place in the country."

So I did. I called Gene. "No," he said, "I don't know."

"But Brown said you would know," I said.

Then Gene, my friend and neighbor from Halifax, who cuts my hay said: "Oh, I bet he meant Gene Gates who lives in Rowe."

"Gee, Thanks," I stammered.

So I called Gene Gates the second! I told him his friend Brown had suggested I call him.

Without a moment's hesitation he told me: "Call Gene Claussen at Miller's Falls Paper Company."

Next morning, I did. "I don't know," said Gene. "I just bought two new stainless steel ones for $400 apiece. But let me look around. If I find anything, I'll call you."

Next day I had to be in Lebanon. On the following day, rather dispiritedly I put in another long distance call to Miller's Falls. "Yes," said Gene, "I tried you twice yesterday and couldn't get you."

"I know," I said. "I had to be away."

Gene continued. "I found an old one. It's only 7 inches from flange to flange you can have it if you want."

Seven inches, I thought, and I need 11 inches between flanges; else I must remount the pump, jack shaft, etc. But I had no other lead, so I said. "I'll be right over and have a look."

June and I climbed into the car, unsure whether we were on a wild goose chase or not. We got to the mill, ten miles east of Greenfield, and sure enough, there it was, full of paper crud. But it could be cleaned up. And Gene said, "You can have it if you want."

I speculated, "I guess I can get flanges at the big junk yard in Greenfield, or from the big supply houses there. Then I have a piece of steel pipe. I'll get Percy to weld the flanges on it and then I'll be in business." So I thanked Gene, loaded my new gate valve in the wagon and went on another scrounging expedition to Greenfield's possible supply sources.

Kramer's junk yard didn't bother with such things—everything was shredded, and reduced to scrap to be recycled. And neither could the plumbing supply houses help. So in desperation, I called Gene back.

"I've been all around," I said, "I can't find flanges anywhere."

"I think I can find a couple," replied Gene, "and if you don't need them today, I'm too busy, I'll fix them tomorrow on a piece of stainless steel pipe 4 inches long." Next day, at 4 o'clock I was back at Miller's Falls, and Gene true to his promise had flanges, the 4 inch piece of pipe, and gaskets all set. I thanked him. He had such a good face. I told him Lincoln's story about the office seeker who importuned him for a postmastership for a friend, whom Lincoln knew.

"I won't do it," said Abe, "I don't like the man's face."

"But surely you can't hold it against the man, the kind of face he had," said the disappointed politician.

"After 40, you can," snapped Lincoln.

Our world is so full of scoundrels, we so often fail to realize that it has more wonderful people than one would ever dream of. And that is the one thing Mr. Murphy can't fix: the boundless goodwill that I found everywhere I asked for help. Because of it, I was back in business. Gene Claussen, with no thought of reward saw a need: he wanted to help.

As soon as we were running—we had to get the thing back on before the ice let go and the powerhouse itself would be washed away—I called Gene and said: "How about coming over and seeing my rig in operation Sunday?" He did. We had a great afternoon, and I have gained another friend, the kind of man who is so important in this world, who makes it a better place in which to live.

The reason I couldn't stop the flow from the top of the penstock was: the ice was so thick, I couldn't get to the slot to drop the plywood stop in. I had "hornswoggled" another gentleman, who stopped by to see the hydro, into coming up into the woods to try to get the gate of the dam free.

John Raymond, an electroplating executive from Connecticut had come to Vermont to get the business cobwebs out of his mind. What balm it was—for him to lie on his belly on the two foot thick ice, cutting chunks with the chain saw, finally getting the gate free enough so we could cut its planks and get the water out. What a pleasant afternoon. See Fig. 13-1.

After spending hours with saw, axe, digging bars, and chest high waders, to finally free up the dam gate, John came

159

Fig. 13-1. Cutting the ice with a chain saw.

back to the house with me—for a spot of tea, it being just 4 o'clock. June had just made some peanut butter chip cookies. They hit the spot. Next day, John called from Connecticut: he had had a safe trip home—and he was sending me some honey he had produced—he knew I'd like such natural foods. Actually, with such experiences, I've come to like Murphy!

All things considered, it is wise for the person proposing to put in his own hydro, to be aware of the trials and tribulations that may await him. Don't build a small hydro with the idea that once built, it will take care of itself. It won't. It needs constant supervision. One's ear becomes attuned to the proper hum of the turbine and generator. What sweet music it is: to hear the turbine, the generator running so effortlessly, using no fuel other than the power of falling water: turning its mechanical energy into electric energy.

When something goes wrong, when the music turns sour, one must be ready with the remedy. Daily inspections are important. Weekly greasings are needed for the jackshaft bearings. But one can't grease these bearings too much, else the grease will leak on the shaft and run on the bearing collar with disastrous results. Once the collar begins to slip, the shaft is ground down, the bearing is ruined, and Murphy has put you out of business. Bearings on the motor-generator and

Fig. 13-2. This is the steaming "ice fountain."

pump-turbine have large grease reservoirs. They need only a shot a month. But daily trips are needed. Does the pump sound right? Has any grit or stream bed debris somehow clogged the runner of the pump? The runner of course, is the part that turns, or runs—driving the shaft from the force of the

Fig. 13-3. Bill Moran (left) producer of the program for CBS television, watches as the camera crew shoots pictures of the inside of the powerhouse through the door.

Fig. 13-4. The Whitingham High School Band played for the dedication exercises, May 10, 1980.

water hitting it. Packing glands on each end of the pump should leak, at least a drop a second for proper cooling and to prevent overheating.

Doubtless other hydro developers have had other encounters with Murphy's law. I don't believe anyone could have had more fun than I. Properly engineered and properly installed, small hydro installations are the most congenial to man's environment of any power source. They do not pollute. They pose no threat to nature. They use a resource which renews itself. Man and nature can live in harmony.

Come with me to the powerhouse in the cool of the evening. Enjoy with me the warmth with its pleasing moist

Fig. 13-5. Several hundred people gathered to witness the throwing of the ceremonial switch by Vermont Electric Cooperative's Executive Manager, William J. Gallagher (photo by Nat Worman).

162

Fig. 13-6. U.S. Senator Patrick Leahy (left) spoke briefly, as did the Chairman of Vermont's Public Service Board. Vermont Electric's Manager, Gallagher (to the right of Senator Leahy) is flanked by William Kinney (just behind the author, J. George Butler) (photo by Nat Worman).

aroma. Listen to the steady hum of the magnetic starter, the subdued whirring of belts and motor, check the figures on the dial of the watt hour meter, and calculate how many kilowatt hours you have generated each day. My watt hour meter registers in 20 kilowatt gradations. When it is up to speed, the dial turns just about 7 times a minute. If it is going less, I know something is wrong somewhere.

But Tom Sawyer was certainly correct: Work consists in what one is obliged to do. Play is what one is not obliged to do. I believe everyone who has visited my "toy" subscribes to Tom's philosophy. I know Steve does, and I know, I do too. See Figs. 13-2 through 13-6.

Chapter 14

The Economics of
Small Scale Micro-Hydro

The price a utility pays for co-generated power is only part of the answer to the question: What are the economics of small scale hydro? Also a part of the picture are: the present energy emergency, the rising cost of other forms of electric energy, as well as conservation and the use of renewable energy sources for the future. To answer the question: will it pay to develop a specific hydro site, one must first look at the overall picture of electric generation of the United States. The New England situation is different from the rest of the nation, because it, more than any other region in the "lower 48" is without fossil fuel resources and dependent therefore on imports for most of its energy. In this discussion, I refer not to the over-all energy picture, including transportation, but solely that segment used for the production of electric power.

SOURCES OF ELECTRIC POWER GENERATION

Through the courtesy of the U.S. Department of Energy, I have obtained the statistical breakdown of sources of electric generation from 1972, to 1979. See Fig. 14-1.

Look first at the pie charts for 1972. The first, most striking fact is that coal was still king, accounting for 44.2% of

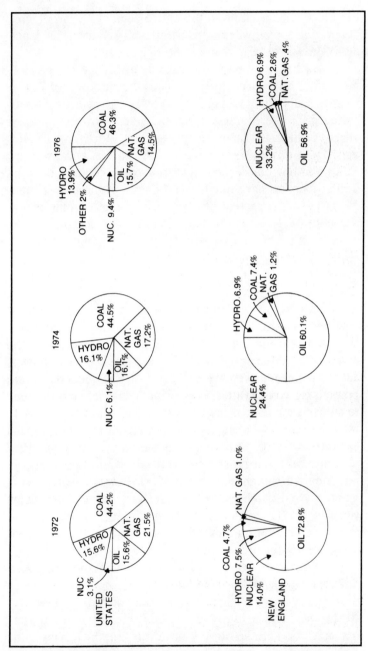

Fig. 14-1. These pie charts show the sources of electric power generation in both United States and New England (courtesy of D.O.E.).

165

the electric generation in the entire country. Hydroelectric generation and oil were equal with 15.6%. Natural gas generated 21.5%. Nuclear reactors produced 3.1%.

New England on the other hand, in 1972, was dependent on oil, for nearly three quarters of its electric power or 72.8%. Coal, accounted for 4.7 percent in contrast to nearly ten times as much for the country at large. Nuclear power, was used nearly five times as much to generate electricity in New England as in the rest of the nation. This is because New England is an energy starved section of the country, or so its utility planners have seemed to believe. Hydropower, once New England's greatest asset in the industrial revolution now accounts for less than half the total percentage than in the country as a whole. The geography of New England has not changed. It still has its myriad streams, rivers, once harnessed to give its preeminence in the first part of the nineteenth century.

If one stops to analyze why this is so he comes upon several answers. First, the early factories, grist mills, and sawmills that dotted the New England landscape in the nineteenth century, did not require a great deal of power. Thirty or forty horsepower was all that was needed to grind grain or cut wood. Hence, a growing industrial giant seemed to outgrow small sources of power. The cult of bigness held sway in everything. Bigger was better not only in factories but corporate organization and the generation of power also.

Secondly, one must mention the growing dependence on oil. America had an abundance of oil. It was cheap, convenient, and so much easier to build generating units which were oil fired, versus the costly initial capital expense involved in building massive dams for large hydroelectric installations. The economics of the situation favored oil. Another factor which is important is: many of the abandoned mill sites which dot the landscape all over New England, were deserted by industries leaving the cold, rugged climate of the Northeast, in favor of the warmer climate of the South. Particularly was this so after World War II, when many New England factories loaded their machines and equipment onto

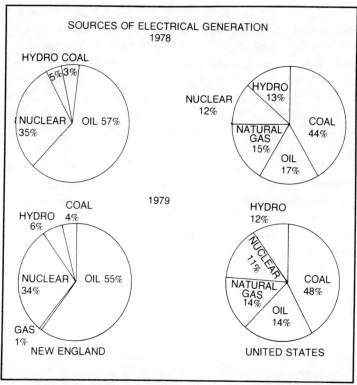

Fig. 14-2. Sources of Electric Generation in the years, 1978, 79, shows significant trends. Coal increased both for the U.S. and New England, while nuclear generation declined (courtesy of D.O.E.).

flat cars and moved south not only for reasons of climate which meant lower fuel costs, but also because of cheap labor.

In 1933 President Roosevelt signed the Tennessee Valley Authority bill, long the dream of Senator George Norris, with the result that an entire seven state region of the nation had a federal yardstick for the cost of power. Originally designed for hydropower, the TVA quickly attracted many industries from the Northeast where there was no such federal yardstick for power.

Electric utilities in New England, had been successful in keeping all Federal power projects out of the Northeast. As a result, though many flood control dams have subsequently been erected in the area not one until now has been given the capability of hydroelectric generation a practice common in the rest of the country.

While a diligent search is now underway to rediscover this huge energy potential which once made New England great, it takes a long time to plan, engineer, and construct such facilities. In addition, as the economic picture changes, and renewable energy from hydro becomes increasingly more attractive, there must be a change of mindset, from the "bigger is better" idea.

As one compares the changes in the sources of electric power from 1972 to 1979 one must bear in mind the long leadtime required for such a transition. When oil goes in price from $1.80 a barrel to $40 in 1981, an increase of more than 22 times, the economics of electric power has suddenly been stood on end.

As with gasoline, people have quickly discovered: we have rationing by price. They can't afford to use it as prodigally as they once did. So too with electricity. From an annual growth rate of 7 percent a year, electric demand has been scaled back to about 3 percent, Utilities have found conservation far cheaper than building new plants.

Even coal fired power plants are expensive to build, though more and more utilities seem to be turning to coal as the fuel of choice, as one studies these charts. From 44.2 percent of the total in 1972, coal generated power accounted for 48 percent in 1979, jumping four percentage points in the one year alone, 1978 to 1979. In contrast to this, nuclear power, which rose steadily in its percentage of total production until 1978, dropped off from 12 percent to 11 percent in the last year for which we have figures. Whether this represents a trend for the future remains to be seen. Some analysts, contrary to the Electric Power Research Institute which still believes nuclear power to be the cheapest option have statistics to show nuclear reactors are no longer competitive with coal fired plants. Whatever kind of generation is decided on however, until cheap, commercially available solar electricity is produced in sufficient quantity, the cost of electric energy is simply going through the roof.

The testimony of the market place is: nuclear power is no longer the cheapest option, and no new nuclear plants have been ordered in the U.S. in the past two years. It is instructive if we follow the reasoning of the Electric Power Research Institute and see what the costs of nuclear power might be in 1990, if indeed, this is the cheapest form of electric power available. The price this electricity must sell for, is the yardstick by which one measures his own hydro plant which he contemplates.

ESTIMATED COSTS OF ELECTRIC POWER BY 1990

The Vermont Electric Cooperative, Inc., on whose Board I sit, like all New England utilities is caught in the cost squeeze of trying to provide sufficient baseload generating capacity by the end of the decade. Nuclear plants which were built in the early 1960s at a cost of $134 a kilowatt of installed capacity—the way the industry measures cost—are now costing well over $2000 a kilowatt. For instance, the Co-op Board recently voted to buy an additional 4.8 megawatts of Seabrook II (New Hampshire) and Millstone III (Connecticut) for $2062.50 a kilowatt of installed capacity. And projections for the Shoreham nuclear station on Long Island, said to be the costliest nuclear plant in the nation are for it to cost $2700 a kilowatt of capacity. The present cost of power to the Co-op, taking its entire mix, from the low cost hydropower from the Power Authority of the State of New York, at 7 mills a kWh, to 45 mills for gas turbine peaking power, averaging about 28 mills was sold to the consumer for an average of about 6c a kilowatt hour last year. Now, the Co-op, like every other utility in the land, has to ask for rate increase after rate increase to pay the added costs. In a few years it expects to have a capital structure of $50 million, compared with an investment today of just over $17 million. In other words, to pay interest on such a capital expenditure will necessitate rates doubling or even tripling by 1990. Rates of 20¢ a kWh will not be out of line.

One large New England Utility, projecting the cost of electricity from an oil fired, peaking power unit it expects to build for 1991 standby emergency service, puts that cost at 32¢ a kilowatt hour. And the Co-op which hopes to bring power from an Army Corps of Engineers' dam, which is already built, on line by the mid 80s, projects that the generating facilities and necessary modifications to the dam will raise the cost of that power to the utility to 14½¢ a kWh.

Though these figures may seem high to the Pacific Northwest and the TVA which have the lowest power costs in the nation, they are not high to those who live in New York City where Consolidated Edison is charging 12¢ a kWh.

One device which utilities are increasingly using, and which the Public Utilities Regulatory Policy Act encourages, is, for utilities to charge higher rates in winter, to discourage use, and lower peak consumption of power. If a new rate design which has been filed by the Co-op goes into effect, our rates will practically double in winter, from the 4.9¢ a kWh they will be in summer. Last year, the Wall Street Journal reported utility rate increases topped $5 billion, surpassing 1979's previous record of $3.1 billion. The bottom line of this story is: " . . . Analysts . . . estimate that restoring the companies (utilities) even close to financial health would require rate increases of $5 to $8 billion a year *beyond* any increases designed to keep pace with rising costs . . . " In another story, the Wall Street Journal analyst projected electric rates to triple in the decade. Hence, for the purposes of calculating:" is it worthwhile for me to build my hydro plant? "take as an assumption the cost of electric power in 10 years, wherever you live, to be probably three times what it is today.

BENEFIT TO COST RATIO FOR SMALL HYDRO PLANTS

With the foregoing discussion in mind, what then is it reasonable to expect in the way of economic return from one's investment in hydro? Since Murphy's law has a way of obtruding itself in the nastiest fashion, one must consider economics—the dismal science, in its most dismal terms. Suppose we have drought for the rest of the century. Some meteorologists seem to want to vie with Malthus and his dire predictions. At any rate, according to these disciples of doom, their sunspot theory predicts that sunspots will be evident for the rest of the twentieth century, and that these sun spots are the cause of the present drought. In such a case, deficits similar to this year's deficit of 12 inches rainfall will continue for the next two decades. In that case I may be able to run my hydro for only six months each year.

The net generation for six months would be something like 10 kW an hour, times 24 hours a day, times 30 days a month or 7200 kWh a month. Multiply this by six months and one would have 43,200 kWh annually, assuming one ran only 6 months a year.

How much is such power worth? Though the Public Service Board held hearings Dec 29, and 30, 1980 and was supposed to render its decision as to the rates to be paid to co-generators by utilities, a phone call this afternoon revealed that no decision has as yet been reached. What the PSB will decree is anyone's guess.

Compare electricity to the price of oil—yesterday the oil truck pulled up and delivered 80 gallons at $1.31 a gallon. When the hydro was not running, he left 260 gallons. On the basis of this price a kilowatt supplants enough oil to be worth 5¢, for the equivalent heat value. So, based on that value the electricity generated is worth $2160 a year. At that rate, the payout period would be just over eight years. Once capitalized however, my project becomes a "gold mine." As a matter of fact, even now, it is worth far more than that. Figure its worth in terms of the energy it saves me from purchasing from the Co-op. Winter rates now begin at 10¢ a kWh. On that basis, I would save about $100 a month during the winter on electric bills, plus the value of the oil I did not burn. And the cost of oil, and electric rates will rise rapidly.

For one interested in calculating the electric equivalency to oil, figure the net British Thermal Units (BTUs) in a gallon of oil (90,000) divided by the net BTU's in a kilowatt of electricity, 3420. That is, it takes 26.314 kilowatts to produce the same thermal value of oil burned in the furnace of average efficiency. To find the price as related to the price of oil, divide the current price of oil per gallon by this figure 26.314.

Should my assumption of the worst case scenario prove wrong, and we have normal rainfall so that I can run at least 9 months every year, the payback of capital cost (without interest) would take 5.3 years. But suppose we go to the year 1990. By then a kilowatt will be worth 20¢ or more. Hence, my 43,200 kilowatts in 6 months would be worth $8,640. And if I am able to operate at least 9 months my kilowatts would be worth $12,960 a year.

Of course this is "speculation", but not "idle speculation." It is a darned good "speculation" or investment if you prefer, call it what you will. For my hydro will still be turning out the kilowatts long after I am dead and gone. If anyone is interested in doing likewise, the sooner he begins, the better off he'll be.

Since two thirds of my cost of $17,500 was incurred with the dam and half mile plus of penstock anyone with a shorter pipe run would stand to gain significantly on the cost side. Currently, utilities are spending billions. The Wall Street Journal estimates their investment over the next ten years to be at least $600 billion, even with demand scaled back to 2 or 3 percent growth a year, to meet power demands. Any power which can be co-generated, will save the utility at least $2,000 in capital expense for each kilowatt, and probably more, as each year passes. Thus, from an economic standpoint small scale hydro such as I have built seems to be a sure fire investment for the future as well as making a contribution to the energy crisis facing America.

Chapter 15

Rates Paid to Co-Generators

Those who are contemplating building a small or micro-hydro system should know how much they might be paid for the electricity they sell to the utility. Back in 1977, New York State told Consolidated Edison it had to buy the surplus power from a 2 kW windmill atop a Manhattan rehabilitated tenement. Even a 2 kW hydroplant running for a month will produce 1440 kilowatt hours, far more than the average family uses in a month.

Small hydro installations of less than 10 kilowatts are exempt from regulation as utilities by the Public Utilities Regulatory Policy Act of 1978, (PURPA). According to it, they are eligible for both energy and capacity payments from utilities which must purchase their surplus power.

In Sections 201 and 210 of PURPA, rules for implementing the provisions of the act were adopted in Feb. 1980 by the Federal Energy Regulatory Commission (FERC). State regulatory bodies were directed to set "reasonable rates reflecting both avoided energy and capacity costs" of the utilities. In a study by J.C. Van Kuiken, of the Argonne National Laboratory, (for the Department of Energy) these rates are given on a state by state basis. Examining the rates in this table (See Table 15-1) look for example at the rates for the Pacific Gas and Electric Co. in California. Various energy payments are

Table 15-1. Rates Paid for Power Purchased by Qualifying Cogenerators (courtesy of Glenn Lovin International Cogeneration Society and U.S. Dept. of Energy).

State	Utility (Electric Reliability Council)	Energy Payments (c/kWh)	Capacity Payments ($/kW-yr)	Retail Rates[a] (c/kWh)	Comments[b]
ALA	Alabama Power Co. (SERC)	2.61; on-peak, June-Oct 1.88; off-peak, June-Oct 2.20; on-peak, Nov.-May 1.77; off-peak, Nov.-May		5.41	Nuclear 24%, Coal 58%, Oil 1% Gas 3%, Hydro 14% Off-peak purchase rates are offered for facilities without time-of-day (TOD) metering. Rates are for facilities less than 100 kW.
ARK	Arkansas Power & Light Co. (SWPP)	reverse metering currently used		5.60	Nuclear 17%, Coal 9%, Oil 44%. Gas 10%, Hydro 20% Comments on proposed rates due by April, 1981
CAL	Pacific Gas & Electric Co. (WSCC)	4.682; on peak, May-Sept 4.504; partial-peak, May-Sept. 3.878; off-peak, May-Sept. 4.496; on-peak, Oct-Apr 4.250; partial-peak, Oct-Apr 3.794; off-peak, Oct-Apr	55-81 for dispatchable capacity (increases with length of contract 4-30 yrs); other options available for non-dispatchable capacity.	8.46	Nuclear 4%, Oil 67%, Gas 1%, Hydro 25%, Other 3%
	San Diego Gas & Elec. Co. (WSCC)	7.748; without TOD metering 8.457; on-peak 7.174; semi-peak 6.317; off-peak	0-40 depending on availability and contract length (1-25 yrs). Incentive capacity payments: $/kW-mo. Capacity factor .00 0-14% .70 15-49% 1.30 50-85% 2.00 85-100%	10.65	Purchase rates are essentially for 1980 and for facilities 100 kW or less

CONN				
Connecticut Light & Power Co. and Hartford Elec. Light Co. (NPCC)	*Firm Power:* 6.7: on-peak equals 114.5% of fossil fuel cost 5.4; off-peak equals 90.5% of fossil fuel cost *Non-Firm Power:* 6.6: on-peak equals 110% of fossil fuel cost 5.2; off-peak equals 86.5% of fossil fuel cost		5.15 5.41	Nuclear 38%, Oil 60%; Hydro 2% Purchase rates are temporarily in effect pending approval of utility proposals. Firm-power rates are for facilities greater than 100 kW. Off-peak purchase rates are offered for facilities without time-of-day metering. No size restrictions apply to non-firm facilities.
IDAHO				
Utah Power & Light Co. (WSCC)	*Firm Power:* 1.2 *Non-Firm Power:* 2.2	88-266 increasing with contract length 4-35 yrs.	6.64	Oil 1%, Gas 3%, Hydro 96%. The Idaho PUC has ordered UP&L add some capacity credit to the non-firm energy payment.
Washington Water Power Co. (WSCC)	*Firm Power:* 1.6 *Non-Firm Power:* 2.4	96-280 increasing with contract length 4-35 yrs. .3	1.98	
Idaho Power Co. (WSCC)	*Firm-Power:* 1.639 *Non-Firm Power:* 1.41-3.86 (varies each Month)	116-318 increasing with contract length 4-35 yrs.	2.89	Rates are for facilities less than 100 kW. The Idaho PUC Has ordered IPC to add some capacity credit to the non-firm energy payment.

[a]Note: These are approximate residential retail rates for users with monthly demands of 2000 kWh or greater. Source: Electric Rate and Cost Survey, Residential Service Midwest Research Institute Project No. 7018-T, Nov., 1980, revised Feb. 1981.

[b]"Nuclear, Coal, Oil, Gas, Hydro, and Other" percentages indicate statewide capacity mix.[1]

Table 15-1. Rates Paid for Power Purchased by Qualifying Cogenerators

(courtesy of Glenn Lovin International Cogeneration Society and U.S. Dept. of Energy) (continued from page 175).

State	Utility (Electric Reliability Council)	Energy Payments (¢/kWh)	Capacity Payments ($/kW-yr)	Retail Rates[a] ($/kWh)	Comments[b]
		Rates for Power Purchased from Qualifying Cogenerators or Small Power Producers by State Regulated Utilities (continued)			
KAN	Kansas Power & Light Co. (SWPP)	1.60		6.04	Coal 35%, Oil 11%, Gas 55% Temporary rate in effect since Sept. 1979 prior to finalized implementation rules. These apply to facilities less than 50 kW.
MICH	Statewide purchase rate includes Consumers Power Co. Detroit Edison (ECAR)	2.5		5.33 6.18	Nuclear 14%, Coal 47%, Oil 23% Gas 4%, Hydro 11%, Other 1%. This rate was established prior to PURPA compliance. New purchase rates will be implemented in the future.
MINN	Northern States Power Co. (MARCA)	*Firm Power:* 2.06-3.07 Increasing with contract length 5-25 yrs. *TOD metering service:* 2.15 on-peak 1.39 off-peak *Non-Firm Power* 1.35 *Occasional Power* 1.66		4.70	Nuclear 21%, Coal 55%, Oil 19%, Gas 1%, Hydro 2%, Other 2% Temporary rate schedule in effect until further studies are completed. These rates are intended to comply with PURPA requirements and are restricted to facilities less than 100 kW. Capacity credits are included in Firm Power purchase rates. Non-firm power rates take effect in the event that a Firm product does not provide dependable generation. Occasional Power is limited to 500 kWh/mo. Retail rates not available at time of publication

State	Utility	Rate	¢/kWh	Notes
NEB	Omaha Public Power Dist. (MARCA)	*TOD metering rate:* 1.60, on-peak, summer 1.00, off-peak, all year 1.20, on-peak, winter *Standard Rate:* 1.10	4.36	Nuclear 26%; Coal 46%; Oil 13% Gas 9%; Hydro 3%; Other 3%. Rates apply to facilities less than 100 kW.
NEW HAMP	Statewide rate (NPCC)	*Firm Power:* 8.2 *Non-Firm Power:* 7.7	5.62	Coal 30%, Oil 47%, Hydro 23% Granite State Electric Utility is not required to pay the Firm-Power rate due to excess capacity.
NEW JERSEY	Jersey Central Power and Light Co. (MAAC)	*Approximate only* 6.0-7.5; on-peak 2.0-5.0; off-peak		Nuclear 14%; Coal 13%; Oil 69%; Gas 1%; Hydro 3% Actual rates are determined by averaging marginal energy rates for previous three-month on-peak and off-peak hours. The rate applies to facilities between 10 kW and 1000 kW. Retail rates not available at publication.
	Atlantic City Elec. Co. (MAAC)	*Temporary rate* 2.5	6.80	This Oct. 1980 rate was greater than average energy costs. The utility has proposed that buy-back rates may be set at time of interconnection.

[a]Note: These are approximate residential retail rates for users with monthly demands of 2000 kWh or greater. Source: Electric Rate and Cost Survey, Residential Service Midwest Research Institute Project No. 7018-T, Nov., 1980, revised Feb., 1981.

[b]"Nuclear, Coal, Oil, Gas, Hydro, and Other" percentages indicate statewide capacity mix.[1]

Table 15-1. Rates Paid for Power Purchased by Qualifying Cogenerators (courtesy of Glenn Lovin International Cogeneration Society and U.S. Dept. of Energy) (continued from page 177).

State	Utility (Electric Reliability Council)	Energy Payments (¢ / kWh)	Capacity Payments (¢ / kW-yr)	Retail Rates[a] (¢ / kWh)	Comments[b]
NEW YORK		Note: All New York purchase rates were developed as "illustrative tariffs" pending further investigation			Nuclear 13%, Coal 8%, Oil 63%, Hydro 15%, Gas and Other 1%.
	Long Island Lighting Co. (NPCC)	3.84-4.15, on-peak 3.53-3.33, intermediate 2.29-2.40, off-peak (depending on level of interconnection)	26.0-27.0, on-peak; 2.5, intermediate; 0, off-peak (depending on level of interconnection)	9.25	These rates apply to facilities less than 10,000 kW. Larger facilities will be quoted monthly rates. Levels of interconnection include secondary, primary and transmission in order of increasing value.
	Niagara Mohawk Power Corp. (NPCC)	1.789-6.790; weekdays 1.404-5.509; weeknights 1.165-3.507; weekends (vary with month of year)	determined case-by-case	4.62	Rates apply to facilities less than 100 kW.
	New York State Electric & Gas Co. (NPCC)	3.02; standard rate 3.01-3.18; on-peak 2.60-2.68; off-peak (depending on level of interconnection)			Rates apply to facilities less than 15 kW. Levels of interconnection include transmission, subtransmission, secondary and primary in order of increasing value. Retail rates not available at time of publication.
	Orange & Rockland Utilities, Inc. (NPCC)	3.42-5.07; varies with season and hours of the day		9.80	
	Central Hudson Gas & Elec. Corp. (NPCC)	3.0; standard rate 3.94-4.10; on-peak 3.24-3.38; off-peak (varies with level of interconnection)		6.93	Levels of interconnection are essentially the same as for New York State Elec. & Gas Co. Rates are for facilities less than 100 kW. Larger facilities are charged $15 /mo. for load monitoring.

NORTH CAR.

Note: N.C. Capacity Payments are given as ¢/kWh; not $ as shown above.

Carolina Light & Power Co. (SERC)	2.80-5.55; on-peak 2.07-4.04; off-peak		Nuclear 11%, Coal 71%, Oil 6%, Hydro 12%
Duke Power Co. (SERC)	2.38-5.20; on-peak 1.79-3.91; off-peak		Rates increase with contract length
Virginia Elec. & Power Co. (SERC)	4.23-9.30; on-peak summer 3.59-4.30; peak, non-summer 2.62-5.77; all others	4.35	Rates increase with contract length
Nantahala Power & Light Co. (SERC)	2.05	3.96	Rates increase with contract length NP&L purchases power from TVA

1.49-2.39; summer months
1.29-2.08; non-summer months
1.11-1.66; peak-months
0.66-1.00; off-peak months
1.61-2.50; summer
1.45-2.25, non-summer

2.50

NORTH DAK.

Note: proposed rates - not yet finalized

Northern States Power Co. (MARCA)	2.15, on-peak 1.39, off-peak	4.70	Coal 82%, Oil 4%, Hydro 14% Rates apply to facilities less than 100 kW. Capacity payments increase with length of contract 5-25 years. Facilities larger than 100 kW treated case-by-case.

2.06-3.07 (¢/kWh)

[a]Note: These are approximate residential rates for users with monthly demands of 2000 kWh or greater. Source: Electric Rate and Cost Survey, Residential Service Midwest Research Institute Project No. 7018-T, Nov., 1980, revised Feb., 1981

[b]"Nuclear, Coal, Oil, Gas, Hydro, and Other" percentages indicate statewide capacity mix.[1]

Table 15-1. Rates Paid for Power Purchased by Qualifying Cogenerators
(courtesy of Glenn Loving International Cogeneration Society and U.S. Dept. of Energy) (continued from page 179).

State	Utility (Electric Reliability Council)	Energy Payments (¢/kWh)	Capacity Payments ($/kW-yr)	Retail Rates[a] (¢/kWh)	Comments[b]
OKLA.	Statewide rate schedules includes OK Gas & Elec. Co. Public Service Co. (SWPP)	.86-3.05 depending on firmness of capacity		4.43 4.40	Formula have been established to treat purchase rates for various types of small power producers. Both energy and capacity components are considered.
SOUTH CAR.	Carolina Power & Light Co. (SERC)	2.80; on-peak 2.07; off-peak	46.68; summer 40.20, non-summer	4.35	Nuclear 29%, Coal 30%, Oil 21%, Hydro 19%, Gas and Other 1%. Rates are for facilities less than 5 MW.
	Duke Power Co. (SERC)	1.98; on-peak 1.49; off-peak	60.00 (based on integrated during peak months June-Sept and Dec-Mar).	3.96	
UTAH	Utah Power Light Co. (WSCC)	*Temporary Rate:* 2.2	2.6¢ / kWh	6.64	Coal 86%, Oil 2%, Gas 2%, Hydro 10%. Purchase rates are for facilities less than 1000 kW (100 kW for hydro). Larger facilities are considered case-by-case (up to 3.5¢ / kWh).
VERMONT	Statewide rate schedule (NPCC)	*Proposed Rates Only:* 7.8; standard rate time-of-day rates: 9.0; on-peak 6.6; off-peak			Nuclear 57%, Coal 3%, Oil 16%, Hydro 24%. Avoided costs are higher than would be expected from Vermont's capacity mix due to dispatch and accounting practice of NEPOOL. Retail rates not available at time of publication.

WISC

Wisconsin Power & Light Co. (MAIN)	4.80; on-peak 1.75; off-peak (includes capacity payments)		Nuclear 17%, Coal 59%, Oil 17% Gas 2%, Hydro 5% Purchase rates are for facilities less than 200 kW. Larger facilities are treated case-by- case. Retail rates not available at time of publication.
Madison Gas & Electric Co. (MAIN)	2.75; on-peak, summer 1.50; off-peak, summer 2.22; on-peak, winter 1.50; off-peak, winter	4.60	Purchase rates are for facilities less than 200 kW. Larger facilities are treated case-by- case.
Wisconsin Electric Co. (MAIN)	*Firm Power:* 3.65; on-peak, summer 1.45; off-peak, summer 3.45; on-peak, winter 1.45; off-peak, winter *Non-Firm Power:* 2.90, on-peak 1.45, off-peak	6.13	
Northern States Power Co. (MARCA)	*For 20 kW or less* 1.84; on-peak 1.14; off-peak *For 21-500 kW after 1986:* 1.60; on-peak 1.14; off-peak	4.70	Prior to 1986 the rates for 20 kW and less apply to 21-500 kW. No capacity credits will be paid until after 1986. Facilities greater than 500 kW are treated case-by-case
Lake Superior District Power Co. (MAIN)	$4 / kW-month 1.90 $6.02 / kW-month		Purchase rates are for facilities between 6 and 200 kW. Smaller facilities receive no payments. Larger facilities are considered case-by-case. Retail rates not available at time of publication.

[a]Note: These are approximate residential retail rates for users with monthly demands of 2000 kWh or greater. Source: Electrical Rate and Cost Survey Residential Service Midwest Research Institute Project No. 7018-T, Nov., 1980, revised Feb., 1981.

[b]"Nuclear, Coal, Oil, Gas, Hydro, and Other" percentages indicate statewide capacity mix.[1]

Table 15-1. Rates Paid for Power Purchased by Qualifying Cogenerators
(courtesy of Glenn Lovin International Cogeneration Society and U.S. Dept. of Energy) (continued from page 181).

State	Utility (Electric Reliability Council)	Energy Payments (¢ / kWh)	Capacity Payments ($ / kW-yr)	Retail Rates[a] (¢ / kWh)	Comments[b]
WISC (cont'd.)	Wisconsin Public Service Corp. (MAIN)	1.85; on-peak 1.32; off-peak	to be determined according to characteristics of each facility	5.12	Coal 93%, Hydro 6%, Oil and Gas 1%
WYOMING		NOTE: All of the Wyoming purchase rates are "experimental"			
	Utah Power & Light Co. (WSCC)	*Non-Firm Power:* 2.2 *Firm Power* 2.6 .53		6.64	Purchase rates are for facilities less than 100 kW
	Cheyenne Light, Fuel, and Power Co. (WSCC)		Available or demonstration of demand reduction	2.35	
	Tri-County Elec. Assoc. (WSCC)	1.07			This is a non-generating utility which has based its avoided costs on wholesale supply rates. Retail rates not available at time of publication.
	Montana-Dakota Utilities Co. (WSCC)	.405	Available on demonstration of capacity displacement or demand reduction potential	2.58	

[a]**Note:** These are approximate residential retail rates for users with monthly demands of 2000 kWh or greater. **Source:** Electric Rate and Cost Survey, Residential Service Midwest Research Institute Project No. 7018-T, Nov., 1980, revised Feb., 1981

[b]"Nuclear, Coal, Oil, Gas, Hydro, and Other" percentages indicate statewide capacity mix.[1]

given, depending on time of day. In the next column is the capacity payment which varies according to certain conditions.

To determine the total amount one might receive from his plant, I suggest the following equation; Assume a 5 kilowatt installation which will run 80 percent of the time with 20 percent being allowed for repairs, maintenance, low water, etc. One would then multiply the 720 hours in a 30 day month, by the number of months operation at the various rates, and take 80 percent of this total for the energy component of the payment. To this the annual capacity payment, from $55 to $81 per kilowatt depending on one's contract with the utility, would be added.

Some state regulatory agencies chose to make the payment a lump sum or give the option of dividing the rate between peak and off peak. Again, winter and summer rate differentials, to encourage conservation, also make the computation a bit more complicated. Nonetheless from these figures one may arrive at the approximate payments he may receive, after deducting of course, the power he expects to burn in his home.

PURPA directs utilities to figure their "avoided costs". That often is used only in the present tense. "Avoided costs" in the future will be massive. For instance, the Wall Street Journal, 7/23/81 reported that "rates for large industrial users jumped an average of 22% in the year ended March 30. . . Accounting for the sharpest rate boosts were such oil-dependent utilities as Louisiana P&L (up 46%) and Long Island (N.Y.) Lighting (up 45%)".

In Mississippi, a court challenge brought by a utility questions the right of Congress, through the Public Utilities Regulatory Policy Act to regulate rates paid co-generators. Undoubtedly this case will appear on the fall docket of the U.S. Supreme Court. Since it is not possible to give the determination of the Supreme Court, the next best thing is to assess the validity of the legal arguments.

In a perceptive speech before the National conference on Co-generation at Washington, of the International Co-generation Society, March 19, 1981, the former Associate General Counsel of the Federal Energy Regulatory Commission, Ross D. Ain, and sometime Counsel to the House Committee on Interstate and Foreign Commerce (Now Energy and Commerce) felt that legal precedents would demand the high court's upholding of PURPA. At issue is the constitutionality of Sections 210 (E) and (A) of this 1978 Act.

The first landmark case, according to Mr. Ain was the Attleboro, Massachusetts rate case which occurred in 1927. In this, the Court disallowed the attempt of a state to regulate interstate sales of electricity, finding that the Commerce clause of the Constitution reserved that right to the Federal Government.

Ain said that "although the Federal government had not 'filled the field' of regulation . . . the Federal government was uniquely empowered to regulate these sales . . . The Constitution precluded states from entering this field of regulation." This decision became known as "the Attleboro Gap". It was filled by the Roosevelt Administration's Public Utility Holding Co. Act of 1935.

·Nearly three decades later, in 1964, another landmark ruling was handed down in the case of the City of Colton California and its municipal light plant. Colton obtained its electricity from Southern California Edison. SoCal Edison obtained a very large rate increase from the state public utilities commission. Colton contended that since Southern California Edison obtained part of its power from neighboring states such as Nevada and Oregon, this power was in fact, in interstate commerce and under the jurisdiction of the Federal Power Commission, (now the FERC). The Supreme Court agreed.

This case resulted in greatly increasing the power of the Federal government in fixing electric rates, with the interconnecting electric grids that were developing across state lines. One effect of this was to discourage further, co-generation. If the FERC had jurisdiction over rates, then small producers had to keep their books in accordance with the uniform system of accounts. They had to issue all their securities, bond and stock offerings, in accordance, with FPA regulations, and they had to file all rate schedules with the FPC.

These conditions, coupled with the economies of scale big utility power plants enjoyed, plus cheap oil, made electricity so cheap it simply wasn't worthwhile for co-generators to be frugal or to try to produce their own power. It was cheaper to use central station power. As a result, by 1974, only 4 percent of the nation's electric power was co-generated. Then came the Arab Oil embargo of 1973, and the rapid escalation of oil prices in 1977 and 1978. Conservation and co-generation once again were in vogue, as well as economically practical.

In 1977, Congress recognized that very desirable energy savings could be achieved by using co-generation. Domestic resources could be substituted for foreign oil. And it was for this reason, that Congress enacted PURPA, to encourage co-generation.

It therefore is unlikely, according to Ain, that the Supreme Court will uphold Judge Cox in the Mississippi challenge to PURPA. Cox ruled PURPA was a violation of the 10th Amendment, and a violation of a state's right to regulate utility rates within the state.

Mr. Ain says: "I believe that both 210(a) and 210(e) are Constitutional. Section 210(e) affirms a clearly Constitutional exercise of legislative power to exempt from regulation an area of commerce that has been determined previously by the Supreme Court to be within the Federal domain.

Section 210(a) creates a new, unique scheme of regulation under which a person may buy from and sell to utilities. Therefore, says Ain: "It is unlikely that the Supreme Court will view electric rate regulation to be an integral state function." Furthermore, Mr. Ain points out, the Mississippi case contains no injunction against the enforcement of PURPA by the government. Should there be a ruling against PURPA, it would affect only Mississippi and the parties directly involved. It would not apply to other states which could continue to implement PURPA.

Under dateline, Sept. 8, 1981, Robert Partridge, General Manager of the National Rural Electric Cooperative Association, released a resolution passed by District I, in Pittsburgh, Pennsylvania, August 30-Sept. 1, 1981, calling on Congress to abolish PURPA as an unnecessary regulation and expense to Rural Cooperatives.

It seems that this represents a failure on the part of Rural Electric leaders to understand the potential such co-generation as I have outlined possesses for relieving the energy emergency in America. If micro-hydro is encouraged, millions, indeed billions of dollars of debt and the exorbitant interest charges which must be borne by consumers on that debt can be avoided.

When one considers, that even with a dam in place, the North Hartland hydro project now being undertaken will produce electricity costing the Co-op 14½¢ a kWh, because of the enormous debt. At 12 percent interest, and a capacity factor well below 40 percent, the costs become astronomical. Viewed in such a context, small hydro is a bargain for any utility, and will become more so, as the years pass.

Further, in the chapter on conservation and co-generation it becomes apparent that such dual use of steam from coal or other source not only conserves and saves but makes excellent common sense as well. It is my belief that PURPA should not be abolished but strengthened and small energy producers encouraged in their development of small renewable resources.

Chapter 16

The Promise of the Future

Many people mistakenly believe that all of America's hydro power sites have been developed. Many of the best sites have. But many have not. Alaska is regarded as the land of opportunity because of its North Slope Oil. What is not generally realized is that it has vast hydroelectric potential as yet untouched by man. Additionally, tidal power is available with potential at least as great as presently operating hydro stations in the U.S. The Japanese have been studying how to harness the mechanical energy caused by the motion of the waves. Still other scientists are working on hydropower to be generated from the temperature differential occurring in ocean currents, such as the Gulf Stream. For our purposes, let us consider the several options whose technology already exists, and which appear to be the most feasible and available to the United States.

LARGE HYDRO'S POTENTIAL

In 1975 the otherwise excellent Massachusetts Department of Energy's Study dismissed hydro with these words: " . . . Hydroelectric power and natural gas are both important sources in other parts of the country, but both are unavailable for further New England large-scale generation."

In 1977, the Connecticut Public Utilities Control Authority study into *The Economic Aspects of Nuclear Electric Generation* came to the same conclusion: " . . . while hydropower generation is expected to increase in the future the contribution from this source will amount to only about 6% of the total production in the year 2000."

Even so excellent a study as "A Report on New England Hydroelectric Development Potential by the New England Federal Regional Council," in cooperation with the Army Corps of Engineers, is quite incomplete. Although this study indicated 3,000 small dams in New England, six feet or more in height and a storage capacity of at least 50 acre feet, it said it would be good if these sites might be really studied to see what potential they did possess. Since such a study would be "an extensive and costly undertaking" the Army Engineers suggested that one site be selected in each state, explored thoroughly, so that a handbook might be developed for those interested in carrying the idea further.

The book: "Hydropower: A National Energy Resource, Proceedings, March,11-16 1979, sponsored by the Engineering Foundation in cooperation with the U.S. Army Corps of Engineers gives a far more complete assessment of the hydropower potential in Vermont. See Table 16-1. The total potential hydropower in Vermont, according to this study is 467,700 kilowatts.

But even this study is far from exhaustive. Such sites as Halifax's proposed municipal hydroelectric project, for which feasibility studies are now in progress has a potential of at least 700 kilowatts. And in my immediate home region there are many brooks which would lend themselves to the kind of development I have shown practical.

David Lilienthal's article in the Smithsonian Magazine, Sept. 1977, relies on figures from the Federal Power Commission, which exclude all sites of less than 5,000 kilowatts. His estimate thus is conservative. When his article was written, hydro accounted for 16 percent of America's electrical generation. According to Lilienthal, "the Federal Power Commission study asserted that the United States has

Table 16-1. Vermont's Undeveloped Hydro Sites (courtesy of Vermont Electric Cooperative Inc.).

Site	River	Capacity (kW)	Average Annual Energy (MWh)	Capacity Factor	Gross Static Head (feet)	Drainage Area (sq mi)	Average Annual Flow (cfs)
1 Highgate	Missisquoi	7,000	26,000	.42	42	815	1,580
2A Sheldon Springs	Missisquoi	7,700	46,000	.68	106	801	1,550
3 East Richford	Missisquoi	3,000	14,500	.55	40	350	730
4 Sheldon	Black Creek	800	4,100	.59	35	122	230
5 Tyler Branch	Tyler Branch	700	3,600	.59	58	59	110
6A Jay Branch	Missisquoi	4,300	21,900	.58	150)		
6B Jay Branch	Missisquoi	7,300	18,500	.29	166)	132	260
7 Milton	Lamoille	10,000	22,000	.25	95	691	1,260
8 East Georgia	Lamoille	10,000	23,000	.26	45)		
8A East Georgia	Lamoille	6,000	22,900	.43	45)	686	1,220
8B East Georgia	Lamoille	4,100	18,000	.50	35)		
9 Ithiel Falls	Lamoille	1,500	4,000	.30	25	371	680
10A Johnson	Lamoille	1,100	3,000	.31	32	289	630
10B Johnson	Lamoille	2,700	7,000	.30	36	289	630
11 Westford	Browns River	500	700	.16	29	75	150
12 Gihon River	Gihon River	4,000	8,200	.23	250	55	110
13 Green River	Green River	1,000	600	.07	70	16.5	30
14 Garfield	Green River	4,500	4,000	.10	500	18	35
15 Wild Branch	Wild Branch	1,000	1,800	.21	90	30	50
16 Burlington	Winooski	6,000	30,000	.57	54	1,060	1,540
17 Winooski Gorge	Winooski	6,000	15,000	.29	43	N/A	1,540
18 Bolton Gorge	Winooski	6,500	31,000	.54	62	835	1,190
19 Moretown	Mad	2,700	8,600	.36	91	125	240
20 Huntington Falls	Otter Creek	17,400	67,000	.44	135	N/A	N/A
21 Timmouth	Otter Creek	4,000	7,700	.22	510	17	35
22 Vernon	Connecticut	8,400	41,000	.56	34	6,266	10.720
23 Williamsville	West	145,000	84,000	.07	224	407	620
24 Ball Mountain	West	20,000	70,000	.40	340	172	260
25 Springfield	Black	7,000	21,000	.34	122	N/A	N/A
26 Perkinsville	Black	10,000	30,000	.34	220	N/A	N/A
27 Hart Island	Connecticut	25,200	109,000	.49	28	4,633	9,860
28 Gaysville	White	10,700	33,000	.35	139	226	240
29 Wilder	Connecticut	8,100	5,500	.08	51	3,375	7,180
30 Wells River	Connecticut	10,000	30,000	.34	29	N/A	N/A
31 Browns Mill	Paul Stream	9,000	15,000	.19	327	51	90
32 Coos	Connecticut	12,000	50,000	.48	120	N/A	N/A
33 Canaan	Connecticut	7,000	20,000	.33	50	377	640

Source: *Report to Vermont Electric Cooperative, Inc., Power Study, Phase I, Part II, Hydroelectric and Pumped Storage Potential,* prepared by Acres American, Inc., July, 1976.

113,000 megawatts of undeveloped hydro potential, almost twice the 66,000 megawatts of existing capacity."

Lilienthal, who spent a good part of his life building big hydroelectric systems, said "bigness" and "smallness" are not exclusives, but rather "complimentary." In a letter to me, Dec. 15, 1976, Mr. Lilienthal wrote: "I share your belief that the development or redevelopment of small hydro sites will make a most valuable contribution to our energy resources, especially in the New England states . . . "

When one considers that China, a "backward" country, i.e., under-developed, reported five years ago, that it had 70,000 small hydro stations, turning out on average but 42 kilowatts, but aggregating 3,000,000 kilowatts, isn't it time

America woke up to the potential of this kind of energy? With America's wealth and technology, this power of falling water can once again be harnessed.

Alaska is usually thought of as an oil-rich state. What is not generally known is that it is one of the richest regions in its hydropower resources. According to Rural Electric Magazine, Nov. 1979, " . . . 79 hydro projects with a total estimated capacity of 180 billion kilowatts have been identified in the state . . . "

Add to that, the practically limitless energy potential from tidal power projects, such as Cook's Inlet, Alaska, and Passamaquoddy in Maine, where as much water flows into the Bay of Fundy on one tide, as flows down the Mississippi River above New Orleans in two weeks, and one must conclude: hydropower energy resources still abound.

One scheme at Cook's Inlet would involve 1200 square miles of sea and produce about 75 billion kilowatt hours of electricity annually, an amount equal to 7 percent of that used in the entire United States in 1970.

PASSAMAQUODDY

The tidal project of Passamaquoddy has captured the imagination of engineers for more than 60 years. In the 19th century, tide mills dotted the coast of Maine throughout its entire distance. As a frequent visitor to the coastal environs of Bath and the New Meadows I had seen the stone foundations of several of these mills: Berry's Mill, the remains of an old tide mill in the Basin, just off the New Meadows River, in Phippsburg Maine, and John Morse's tide mill which turned his sawmill just below Bath on the Kennebec (finally abandoned in 1936, when cheap electric power displaced it).

Back in 1919, the Bay of Fundy saw the first attempt to harness its tides for hydroelectric generation, with the formation of the Petitcodiac Tidal Power Co. In this same year, an American Engineer, Dexter Cooper began his long work on Passamaquoddy, which straddles the Maine-New Brunswick border. Finally, in 1934, President F. D. Roosevelt approved a $45 million project to harness these tides at Passamaquoddy. In 1935, after $7 million was spent, the project was halted amid charges of "boon-doggle," and the greatest pork barrel ever.

In 1950 a joint U.S.-Canadian commission again examined the scheme, and in 1952 the Army Engineers reviewed it. In 1956, an International Joint Commission spend three years studying it. It finally recommended a 300 megawatt plant at Cobscock Bay. In 1960, another study envisioned a new idea: by using a series of two pools, continuous generation could be accomplished, rather than having hours lost when slack water occurred between ebb and flood tides. In early planning the huge Dickey-Lincoln project on the St. John River was to take care of power demands during this hiatus between tides. With two pools however one would be drained to low tide level while the other would be at flood. With reverse turbines, capable of turning in either direction, it would thus be possible to generate continuously.

This 1960 study suggested as many as 100 turbine generators, each of 10 megawatt capacity, capable of turning out 1,000 megawatts. The cost then was estimated to be $900 a kilowatt, about twice the cost of other power plants. Because of various problems not the least being the political cooperation of the United States and Canada, the project has never been built.

In 1966 however, Canada drew up an intergovernmental agreement creating the Atlantic Tidal Power Programming Board and the Atlantic Tidal Power Engineering and Management Committee. This study lasted three and a half years, and culminated in an International Conference on the Utilization of Tidal Power, held in May, 1970, at Halifax, N.S. Canadian experts were joined by men from England, Russia, France, Germany, and the Netherlands as well as the United States.

The environmental assessments of the project brought joy to all concerned. They found out that fish could pass through the faster turbines in Scotland's hydroelectric plants: and thus, such a tidal project would not have a bad effect on fisheries. Furthermore, the oyster and clam beds actually seemed to benefit, and the project would reduce sedimentation and other changes. The Conference found out that

Russia's experimental tidal plant above Murmansk in the Arctic Ocean had also been used as a herring trap.

Back in 1966 France built a tidal power project on the French Coast of the English Channel. Simpler in design than the continuous generation capability envisaged for Passamaquoddy, this plant at St. Lo on the Rance River has been used for peaking power and though rated at 240 megawatts, has turned out 70 megawatts on average. In addition to the Russian 400 kilowatt experimental project in Kislaya Guba near Murmansk, the Chinese are thought to have about 110 small tidal power plants providing power for farms and small communities.

HYDRO-QUEBEC

Several years ago, I wrote Hydro-Quebec to find out the present status of Canada's thinking on tidal power. Presently

Fig. 16-1. East part of the underground powerhouse (courtesy Hydro Quebec).

Fig. 16-2. West view of the underground powerhouse (courtesy Hydro Quebec).

Quebec is engaged in the largest hydroelectric project in North America, La Grande Complex at James Bay. This project, the first unit of which came on line in 1980, will consist of four power stations, totalling 10,190,000 kW, with an annual production of 68 billion kilowatt hours. Scheduled for completion by 1985, this project has not displaced the Bay of Fundy project entirely in Canadian thinking. See Figs. 16-1 through 16-8. Hydro-Quebec wrote me in February 1978 and said that in 1969 the Bay of Fundy project was deemed too costly. Now, it is being restudied, both by the Canadian Federal Government, and the two Atlantic Provinces, Nova Scotia and New Brunswick, and the results of this study

Fig. 16-3. South part of the main dam (courtesy of Hydro-Quebec).

should be available shortly. Meanwhile, the U.S. Department of Energy has recently made a grant to the Passamaquoddy Indians for a small, pilot project on Cobscook Bay.

Though the cost of such a gigantic undertaking as Passamaquoddy dwarfs the $40 million figure envisioned by President Roosevelt, as well as the $900 a kilowatt of capac-

Fig. 16-4. Aerial view of the spillway (courtesy of Hydro Quebec).

Fig. 16-5. Generators in the underground powerhouse (courtesy of Hydro Quebec).

ity estimated in 1960, the time will doubtlessly come when such colossal tidal power will be harnessed. The only thing that will prevent it is a scientific breakthrough in solar generated electricity, and/or nuclear fusion.

Fig. 16-6. This is one of the turbine wheels (courtesy of Hydro Quebec).

195

Fig. 16-7. These are the diversion channels (courtesy of Hydro Quebec).

SUMMARY

Whatever may be the future of large scale hydroelectric projects in America, small scale hydro is exciting more interest than ever. The December 1980 Small Hydro Bulletin,

Fig. 16-8. The powerhouse under construction (courtesy of Hydro Quebec).

DOE, reports: "The Federal Energy Regulatory Commission continues to receive applications for license and preliminary permits at an unprecedented rate . . . currently the FERC has pending almost 700 projects having a total estimated installed capacity of over 16 million kW.

"Interest in the development of existing dams continues to increase. Of the 700 projects presently before FERC, 94 percent involve the use of an existing dam. The trend toward development of smaller projects also continues. The FERC attributes this intense interest in hydropower development, especially small scale projects, to its new, simplified licensing procedure and permit requirements, the economic incentives enacted by Congress in the last two years, the recent dramatic increases in fuel costs, particularly oil, and the opposition to nuclear power." Add to this, the potential for micro-hydro, such as mine, and America could well be on its way to electric energy self-sufficiency without the use of scarce and costly oil.

Chapter 17

Examples of Small Hydro

The other evening a friend visited us. Formerly with David Lilienthal's Development and Resource Co., now a business man running the Hydropower Development Center of Brattleboro Vermont he startled me with the statement that within a 100 mile radius of Brattleboro Vermont there were 900 megawatts of undeveloped hydropower. Whether his estimate is too optimistic or not I do not know. Such things as capacity factors would have to be examined, benefit to cost studies made to determine economic feasibility, and so on. What I do know is: there are many sites available just waiting to be developed and which can be made to produce energy, economically using this renewable non-polluting resource. In this chapter, I thought it would be worthwhile to show several such projects in my neighborhood to illustrate various ways people have taken to develop these fast flowing streams.

RAY MILLER'S TWO INSTALLATIONS

Raymond C. Miller is a most unusual person. Several years ago, he wrote a book, *Energy from Brook Motors* which he published privately. In it he tells of his lifelong interest in water wheels and water power. At the age of 18 he built his first Pelton wheel and now, something like four decades later, he is still at it. Miller is a man of many interests. By trade a master machinist, he is also a part-time preacher, having studied for awhile at Bangor Theological Seminary. Presently employed by G. and S. Precision Co., of Wilmington and Brattleboro Vermont, Miller has amassed a wealth of information about electricity and hydropower. Years ago he owned a beautiful camp in the wilds of Halifax Center Vermont. Its present owner, Jeremy G. Freeman showed me what Ray had done.

In the 19th century Halifax was a thriving town. At one time, it was the fourth largest in Vermont. One of its industrial establishments of this era was the Dennison Manufacturing Company, which made furniture in a four story mill at a beautiful gorge several miles beyond the old center of town, now almost deserted except for several residents and a beautiful white church which is open only for a few events each summer.

Miller had developed part of the power at the Dennison gorge on his brook and used it to heat his camp which he built there. His penstock was unique, consisting of perhaps two dozen old galvanized hot water boilers, the type I remember from childhood, being connected to the water back on the kitchen range. See Figs. 17-1A, 17-1B, and 17-1C.

With amazing ingenuity Miller had made this penstock with 12″ diameter and 60 feet of head. Constructing a small

Fig. 17-1A. This ingenious penstock was built out of hot water boilers welded together.

Fig. 17-1B. This is another view of the hot water boiler penstock.

shack at the side of the stream, Miller used his own homemade Pelton wheel to turn a 5 kilowatt war surplus dc motor, which gave him plenty of heat for his small summer camp.

But Ray's sights were set on bigger things. Jeremy Freeman, a real estate man in Brattleboro, who now owns this site, was able to find Ray the exact location he wanted: the old Harrisville mill and dam on the Hinesburg Road several miles away, which had far greater potential for year round power.

Jerry Freeman, now confronted with the energy crunch, as we all are is determined to develop this beautiful spot along the lines I have suggested. While Ray used part of the available head, it appears that it is quite feasible to obtain 100 feet of head. With a 12" penstock, or even an 8" it seems very possible that Jerry can develop 20 kW, for his house needs and also to feed back into the Vermont Electric lines.

As a precaution, I suggested that such sharp angles as occur in this hot water boiler penstock should be avoided, so as to lessen the friction loss from such bends. Also, iron pipe becomes rusty and rough, causing far more friction loss than with smooth pvc pipe.

MILLER'S HARRISVILLE DAM

In his book, Ray tells of his rebuilding the old Harrisville Dam to Army Corps of Engineers' specifications (see Fig. 17-2). Instead of a penstock Ray uses the far less expensive canal method with the trash rack right before the mill. The old mill having burned. Miller rebuilt the present one using the upstairs for living quarters and downstairs for his workshop and generating facilities. See Fig. 17-3.

Fig. 17-1C. This is the hot water boiler penstock as seen from the dam.

Fig. 17-2. The old Harrisville Dam on the Green River was restored by Mr. Miller and once again put to use to provide power.

As in so many low head installations, Miller has used a draft tube on the exhaust side to pull the water through the propeller turbine. By using such a conical tube, with its large end submerged in the tail race, the suction adds approximately two feet to the available head, a very important addition when working with low head installations. In this case, Miller has about 18 feet with a possible 20 feet in high water.

Fig. 17-3. This is Mr. Miller's workshop. Note the draft tube at the right and the turbine on the bench.

Fig. 17-4. Ray Miller's 5 kW alternator at the Harrisonville mill on the Green River.

Figure 17-4 shows Miller's 5 kW alternator, which he uses in low water. A 10 kW is nearby, to be turned on in normal water flow, and both can be used when enough water is available giving 15 kW in all.

Figure 17-5 shows a turbine being made by Miller in his workshop. With such lowhead applications as Miller's, a propeller type turbine similar to the wheel or propeller in marine propulsion or an electric fan is considered best. Worthington pumps can run successfully on heads of from 20

Fig. 17-5. Close up of a turbine being built by Ray Miller.

to 1000 feet. If one does not have Miller's mechanical ability, their pumps should be seriously considered. See Appendix A for details of Worthington pumps.

With the renewed interest in hydropower, Miller told me that he had eight orders this year for turbines he was making in his spare time.

ALVIN WARNER'S DREAM

One of my fellow trustees at the Vermont Electric Co-op has a magnificent site on the Missisquoi River immediately across the road from his house. With only a three foot dam Al Warner believes he has the potential for 35 kW. The river, with a drainage area of 17½ sq. miles at this site, has a flow on average of 50 cubic feet a second. To provide for generation in low water Al has put in a small 12″ propeller turbine to turn out 5 kilowatts. For normal flow he hopes to use a pump run backwards to turn out approximately 30 kilowatts.

Because the drainage area of this stream exceeded ten square miles Al had to obtain a permit from the Agency of Environmental Conservation and conform to its rules before developing this site.

When I visited him this past summer, he had the footings for the three foot dam in place, and machinery was busy digging the 40 foot long canal for the water to come to the powerhouse. At the powerhouse, the water drops 12 feet to a bulkhead, made of steel, under which are his small and large turbines. The overall head with draft tubes will approximate 20 feet.

Because the canal enables him to do away with the need for a penstock he has been able to cut his costs greatly and estimates that the total cost of the project will be in the neighborhood of $30,000. Figures 17-6 through 17-8 show Alvin Warner's hydro installation.

AN INDEPENDENT INSTALLATION

Another interesting installation, this time without interconnection with a utility, belongs to Eugene O'Neil of South Newfane Vermont. Gene is an unusual young man. He is a commercial flyer and flight instructor. He has a deep spiritual

204

Fig. 17-6. This picture shows Warner atop the footings for his 3 foot dam.

sensitivity and spiritual awareness found in many of the great Quaker spirits of history. He believes there is a spark of the divine in the soul of man which must be nurtured by silent meditation.

Gene moved to Vermont four years ago and literally hacked a homestead out of the 100 acres of Green Mountain wilderness which he bought. He and his wife Nancy are equally concerned for the sanctity of the earth. Far from destroying the wilderness where they have made their home, they seek to live in consonance with it.

Gene is a very practical young man. After serving a hitch in the Navy, he spent all that he had to finance a trip around

Fig. 17-7. The natural falls on the Mississquoi offer an excellent site for low head, high volume. The still unfinished cut for the canal is at right.

the world, developing a sensitivity to all people by a four months stay in a Kibbutz in Jerusalem, and an 8 months sojourn in an Ashram in India.

When he first bought his 100 acres, the only way he could get across the stream to his homesite was on a log. Now, a beautiful sturdy bridge spans the stream and leads to his modern, comfortable home.

Gene's concern has been to live in agreement with nature, not to destroy it. Just above his beautiful bridge is an artistic little dam which blends in with its natural surroundings. It is only three feet high, making a waterfall far lower than many natural falls in the brook (see Fig. 17-9). The penstock's capped dome rises slightly above the dam. In reality, it is a four foot steel cylinder, two feet in diameter, sunk to the side just above the dam. Two lengthwise slits are cut into it for the entrance of the water. Each opening is covered first with inch mesh, then quarter inch hardware cloth. Immediately on the upstream side is solid steel, to help fend off rocks and gravel as they come down in winter. Each fall he must clear out the accumulated debris so that the headworks of his penstock will function. Last winter, his plant ran continuously. In the fall Gene lamented the accumulating

Fig. 17-8. Blasting was necessary to cut through the ledge to make the canal.

leaves that had to be cleaned out. I mentioned to him that on my visit to Vernon I saw that the ancient dam there was still cleaned by men using a wheelbarrow to haul away debris.

I asked Gene if small newts, minnows, and tadpoles get sucked into the quarter inch mesh of his hardware cloth. "No" he said, "The water flows so gently they are able to swim away. Whether it is the smaller volume of water than mine, or

Fig. 17-9. Gene O'Neil's three foot dam with the headworks of the penstock on the left side presents no obstacle to fish since many falls on the stream are higher.

the narrower openings in his headworks, I do not know. At any rate, he has no trouble keeping marine life safe from his installation. I told him of using window screening in front of my hardware cloth to protect aquatic life during spawning season. If one does not, they can be injured by the high velocity of the turbine blades.

Gene laid his penstock on grade, 900 feet to his very small powerhouse. To do this, he had to use 35 pounds of dynamite to blast a path for his pipe so it could be laid on grade. With this linear footage, Gene has 100 feet of head. Using 200 gallons of water a minute he has a maximum capacity of 3.8 kW.

Gene's generator is an alternator which puts out ac current. He is connected to his house several hundred feet away by three strands of #2 wire laid on the ground. In the two years his plant has been in operation, his wire is by now all but covered by leaves. At the house he converts the ac to dc for storage in a battery bank of 12, six volt batteries. He writes: "I feel it would be most helpful to anyone contemplating such a system to forego a 12 volt system in favor of a six volt system as when a charge is going into it the 12 volt system tends to boil off the water which requires constant inspection and refilling if you want to keep the bank operational." Gene has an inverter which was designed by Criss Cookman of Irving Massachusetts who also designed his turbine. The 15 inch Pelton wheel sits in the middle of the tiny powerhouse with its upright shaft having a large wheel on it which drives a smaller wheel on the alternator.

Gene's penstock is six inch pvc pipe far lighter than mine since he has less than half the head. Just before the powerhouse the pipe is split into two four foot diameter sections which enter the powerhouse at opposite sides so that nozzles on the end of each may strike the Pelton wheel blades at 180 degrees. See Fig. 17-10.

Gene built the steel box housing the turbine. To obtain flexibility in low water Gene can either cut one nozzle out completely with a four inch gate valve, or put in smaller nozzles replacing the 4 inch to 1¼ inch with 4 inch to one inch

Fig. 17-10. This is Gene's powerhouse. Note the penstock where iron pipe is used at the T enabling two nozzles to hit the Pelton wheel.

ones. His two gate valves were scrounged from a junk yard in Massachusetts for about $25 each.

The powerhouse itself stands on wooden stilts, which in turn stand on masonry piers by the side of the brook. The waste water falls through the center of the powerhouse floor and cascades back into the brook. The underside of the powerhouse is made with red oak covered with tar and aluminum paint to make it impervious to the discharge water.

Last year, Gene's plant ran continuously without breakdown. Before then however, Murphy's law socked him, as it did me, Gene was the victim of "implosions". That is, instead of exploding, the pipe caved in, due to a blockage at the intake of the penstock, and the draining of the water at the bottom end. To remedy that, Gene has now installed an inch and a half vent sticking up above snow level. If any blockage does occur at the intake from leaves or debris he won't have to buy new pipe again.

Gene estimates his system to have cost him about $5,000 not counting his labor. But after all, when is work, work? Gene subscribes with me, to Tom Sawyer's beliefs—even when it is near zero and one's arms are in ice cold water mending broken pipe. Perhaps the most important item so far

Fig. 17-11. The inside of the powerhouse showing the steel box with a window, encasing Gene's Pelton Wheel.

as cost is concerned was Gene's battery bank of 12, 6 volt batteries, which came to about $2,000.

Gene's alternative, assuming electricity was valuable for his home, was to pay the utility company $15,000 to build a service into his house, plus monthly charges for power. Gene

Fig 17-12. Gene pointing to the spilling water from his powerhouse.

Fig. 17-13. Gene was particularly proud of the way his small dam blended in with nature. This is a view of the dam from his bridge over the stream.

chose the "homemade" route. After all, one of his purposes in coming to Vermont was to be self sufficient as far as possible. And this he has achieved to a remarkable degree. See Figs. 17-11 through 17-13.

Chapter 18

Coal

America has vast coal reserves capable of lasting many hundreds of years. Because of this, the Federal government has spurred the use of coal to replace oil. Many environmentalists have expressed concern over the pollution coal causes. Not only does it cause acid rain, but carbon dioxide from the combustion of coal makes a "greenhouse" effect, thus altering the earth's climate. Fly ash, sulfuric acid, nitric acid and the other hazards associated with coal mining make nuclear advocates maximize coal's drawbacks and aver that coal is far more damaging to the environment than nuclear power.

While it is true that coal does have drawbacks, improved technology has demonstrated that many of its shortcomings may be overcome. And coal does not present the massive threat of nuclear disaster as does a single nuclear accident. Granted that the history of mining is replete with the deaths of thousands from pneumoconiosis (black lung) and mine disasters, Federal mine safety standards have been drastically tightened. Open pit mines, particularly in the west, do not have the hazards to miners that deep mines present. Under present Interior Department policy, many are concerned that environmental laws against desecrating the landscape will be relaxed, and strip mining will again be responsible for vast environmental damage. But coal technology has advanced greatly in the past decade. Utilities which have turned to coal so substantially in the past five years have found new and better methods of cleaning up its combustion than electrostatic stack scrubbers. These additions, while costly, did succeed in making combustion conform to the clean air standards of the Environmental Protection Administration. Methods to clean coal both before and during combustion as well as after the emissions reach the smokestack are proving to be practical.

THE OTISCA PROCESS: CLEANING BEFORE COMBUSTION

For years powdered coal was floated through a water and magnetic slurry mixture to remove impurities, but this method had rather indifferent success. Almost a decade ago, in 1972, Otisca Industries, Ltd., of Syracuse New York was formed as a research and development company to devise a new method of cleaning coal, before combustion. Almost from its inception, American Electric Power, the largest electric holding company in America, joined forces with Otisca to help develop this process and see how it would affect the use of coal. Its first results were promising. American Electric Power is 93 percent coal fired, and if it could use 4% sulphur Ohio coal from its own mines, it would be a giant step forward. Essentially it is quite simple, making use of an elementary physical principal. Coal has a specific gravity of 1.3. (Water's specific gravity is 1) By floating powered coal through a heavy solution with a specific gravity of 1.5, the inventors of this technology felt that they could thus, by making use of this essentially simple idea, separate coal from its impurities. And indeed they did: achieving a removal rate of 60 percent of the sulfur which sank to the bottom of the vat, along with magnetite and other rock, while the coal, being lighter, simply floated off, to be reclaimed and used as boiler fuel.

American Electric Power is now building a full scale test facility at its Muskingum mine in Ohio, with a capacity for cleaning 125 tons of coal an hour to see if it will really work in production.

Apparently one problem encountered is that coal in chemical combination with sulfur may be more difficult to separate. At any rate, tests are proceeding with this process (see Fig. 18-1).

William S. White, Chairman, American Electric Power, in a letter, April 1, 1980, wrote: "Construction of the demonstration coal-cleaning plant utilizing the novel Otisca Process was completed late last year. We are currently in the testing phase of the operation which will continue through this year. Preliminary test results indicate effective reduction of the sulfur and ash in the Muskingum coal . . . During this year's operation, the facility will be fine tuned for optimal operation . . . We are optimistic about the long range potential of this process to allow AEP greater use of the higher sulfur coals available in our service area."

One of the interesting side-benefits from this process has been found to be that coal so cleaned delivers more energy punch, i.e., more BTU's per pound.

PRESSURIZED FLUIDIZED BED COMBUSTION

Another very interesting method of cleaning up the combustion of coal, is the so-called *pressurized fluidized bed of combustion.* In this process, powdered limestone is sprayed into the hot flames, during combustion, effectively cleaning the sulfur from the stack gases. The limestone forms with it to make gypsum, itself a valuable by-product.

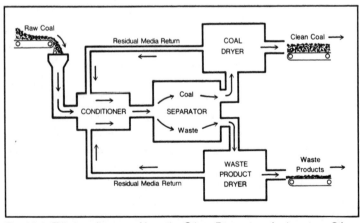

Fig. 18-1. This is a diagram of how the Otisca Process works (courtesy Otisca Industries, Ltd. Syracuse, N.Y.).

Fig. 18-2. This is a model of the atmospheric fluidized bed combustor at Georgetown University, Washington, D.C.

Chairman White wrote of this research (4/1/80) "AEP participated in a 1000 hour PFBC test at a pilot plant in England. The test was designed to assess the environmental impact of the process and to evaluate various materials which could be used in the PFBC combustor and gas turbine. The test results exceeded our expectations. Sulfur reduction during the test period averaged 90 percent. Erosion and corrosion of the test materials were negligible. Based on these favorable results, we are optimistic as to the technical feasibility of the process. We are therefore proceeding with the design and engineering work of a PFBC component test facility. Successful operation on this scale can lead to the construction of a commercial-scale PFBC demonstration plant . . . "

A system similar, to American Electric Power's pressurized, fluidized bed combustion, is that of atmospheric fluidized bed, Georgetown University, under a grant from DOE, installed an experimental coal fired facility of this type (see Figs. 18-2 and 18-3). Georgetown's facility has excited wide interest. Regular tours are scheduled Wednesday mornings. A feature of this plant is, that flyash is reintroduced into the combustion bed where it is burned again, as also with AEP's Pressurized unit, and both claim enhanced fuel efficiency. The same time, they eliminate atmospheric emissions of flyash by a "baghouse" dust collector. When this plant is complete its engineers plan an additional co-generation capability, as the university campus of well over 100 acres provides an ideal set-up for such dual use.

American Electric Power believes its pressurized fluidized bed combustion is preferable to the atmospheric bed, for 'the following reasons:

■ Better overall efficiency through application of a combined cycle, thus reducing coal consumption.

■ Smaller plant size, "permitting shop fabrication of combustors, reducing costs."

■ Lower nitrogen oxide, well within EPA requirements.

In the 1000 hour test at Leatherhead England, AEP found that over 90 percent of sulfur was taken out, combustion efficiency reached an astounding 99 percent, and no erosion or corrosion of the turbine materials was evident. It further concluded that a commercial PFBC plant of 500,000 kW had a 12 percent cost advantage over a conventional coal plant with a scrubber. Accordingly, it is bending all efforts to build and operate its demonstration Tidd plant, presently "mothballed" with the expectation it will be on line in early 1982. In this kind of plant two and a half tons of coal and one and one half tons of dolomite will be fed to the fluidized bed combustor by a pressurized lockhopper injection system.

THE MAGNETOHYDRODYNAMIC PROCESS

Another process with which AEP is experimenting and which demands attention is *magnetohydrodynamics*. This process joins MHD and steam power in one combined cycle plant. The attractiveness of this process says AEP "comes from the fact that the heat in the gas, which is produced by burning coal at high temperature; is converted directly into electric energy without the need for any turbine or rotating generator." Also, the hot exhaust gases can then be used to produce steam which in turn can be used for conventional generation. Such a combination, hopes AEP, "is expected to achieve an over-all generating efficiency in the range of 48 to 60 percent compared with 36 to 38 percent for the best coal, oil or gas-fired power plants and 33 percent for the best

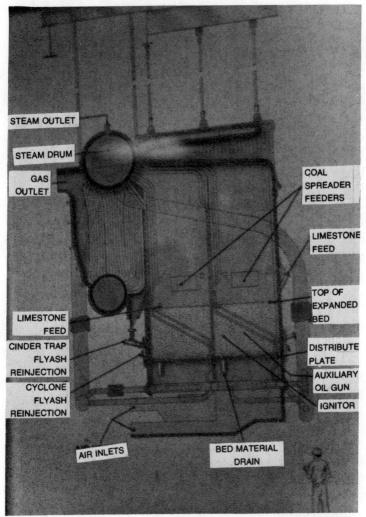

STEAM OUTLET

STEAM DRUM

GAS
OUTLET

COAL
SPREADER
FEEDERS

LIMESTONE
FEED

TOP OF
EXPANDED
BED

LIMESTONE
FEED

CINDER TRAP
FLYASH
REINJECTION

CYCLONE
FLYASH
REINJECTION

DISTRIBUTE
PLATE

AUXILIARY
OIL GUN

IGNITOR

AIR INLETS

BED MATERIAL
DRAIN

Fig. 18-3. This diagram is of a pressurized fluidized bed combustor (courtesy American Electric Power).

nuclear plants. Besides, MHD represents an environmental dividend: it is less polluting that conventional coal-fired generation."

UTAH POWER AND LIGHT'S CHAR PROGRESS

The Washington Spectator, edited by Tristram Coffin, in its May 1, 1980 issue had an arresting article, *Who Controls*

Energy Policy? Coffin wrote: "A team of researchers at Texas A&M has pried open a door to the past, and found clues to inflation and today's price of a gallon of gasoline. "Five years ago the College's Center for Energy and Mineral Resources set out to discover how Nazi Germany fought a great war without major oil resources. This was by a process known as 'coal hydrogenation' which liquefies coal into gasoline and oil. Eighty five percent of the fuel used by Hitler in his blitzkriegs came from synthetic fuel plants." The article continued, telling how after the war, the U.S. found in Frankfurt alone "more than 100 tons of documents . . ."

Though Secretary of the Interior Harold Ickes had funded a pilot plant in 1944 to produce synthetic fuels, the oil industry "successfully blocked" an $8 billion synthetic fuels program. A report of work at an old ordinance plant in Missouri by the Bureau of Mines in 1949 showed that gasoline could be produced by coal hydrogenation for 1.6¢ a gallon. Factoring in inflation, this meant that at today's prices, the cost for a gallon of gasoline from coal would be 15 to 20¢.

In 1953, however, with the discovery of mid-east oil, the oil companies, according to Senator Estes Kefauver did not want this competition, so the Missouri plant was closed and turned over to the Department of the Army for disposal.

Today, Utah Power and Light, a utility without any nuclear capacity, and relying almost entirely on coal, is rediscovering this process. Its 1980 annual report discloses that "The company undertook in 1980 a study of a technology that converts coal into char (a fuel for power plants) in addition to producing a synthetic crude oil. A letter from Arvin Gibson, vice-president in charge of power supply, reads: "In general, the process follows techniques similar to the Lurgi process developed by Germany during World War II to convert coal to liquid fuels. Essentially the coal is heated to about 1000 degrees F. to drive off volatile gases. The residue is char (similar to charcoal) which can be burned in boilers.

"Most of the gases are reclaimed and condensed into a heavy tar which can be treated with hydrogen to become a high-grade crude oil. The crude oil, in turn, can be refined in normal refineries to produce gasoline and other petroleum products.

"The economics of the process are highly dependent upon the characteristics of the coal. Our Utah bituminous coal is particularly well suited for this form of char and synfuel production. For each ton of coal, preliminary tests indicate that we can produce one-half ton of char and one and one-fourth barrels of oil.

"It appears that we may be able to retrofit our Huntington and Hunter 400 MWe units to burn char and produce byproduct oil. Initial studies indicate a potential benefit from the sale of byproduct oil sufficient to decrease our current fuel cost by more than 50 percent.

"We are proceeding in a step-wise fashion on the program in order to minimize technological and economic risks. Our plan includes laboratory tests (many already completed) followed by pilot model and demonstration tests and finally commercial application. We are reassessing the risks and potential economic benefits at each stage. Utah Power and Light Company has sponsored or conducted all the work done to date without assistance from any government agencies. We are very pleased with the results to this point."

In passing, it should be noted that Utah P&L is also exploring the potential of geothermal energy. In 1980, it also signed an agreement with Phillips Petroleum for energy from the Roosevelt Hot Springs near Milford in southwestern Utah for a 20,000 kW pilot test plant, which can come on line as early as 1984 if various Federal approvals are obtained. "Additional units in the 50,000 kW range could follow if sufficient steam is proved and costs are competitive." The company is also studying the utilization of municipal solid waste, as several other utilities are doing.

COAL IN NEW ENGLAND

Because of the lack of coal, oil, and natural gas, New England has been dependent on foreign oil more than any other region of the United States for the generation of electric power. When nuclear power first was proposed, Albert Cree,

President of Central Vermont Public Service Corporation toured the state, touting the virtues of this new technology, averring it would be so cheap it would not have to be metered. So sure was he of this way, he succeeded in keeping cheap hydropower from Churchill Falls Canada from being imported. The result; New England has become more dependent on nuclear generation than the rest of the United States. Now however, with the nuclear option fading, forward looking utility executives are reexamining the use of coal.

On August 27, 1981, the Energy Freedom, the first new barge built specifically to carry coal to New England in more than thirty years arrived at the New England Electric System's Brayton Point Plant, the largest electric station in New England, in Somerset, Massachusetts. It came from Sturgeon Bay, Wisconsin, where it was built, carrying 34,000 tons of coal through the Great Lakes, and the St. Lawrence Seaway. Bringing a load every eight days, the Energy Freedom will carry approximately 1.3 million tons of coal a year, displacing more than 5 million barrels of oil annually, saving $50 million on a yearly basis to the customers of the Massachusetts Electric Company, the Narragansett Electric Company (Rhode Island) and the Granite State Electric Company in New Hampshire, subsidiaries of the New England Electric system.

More important still is the $180 million conversion from oil to coal of the Brayton Point station's third unit so that it too can burn coal. This, when fully completed, will save 12 million barrels of oil, and approximately $169 million for the New England Electric System's retail customers.

New England electric also revealed in this same news story that it is converting three units of its Salem Harbor Station in Salem, Massachusetts, from oil, to coal. This plant will then burn 3.7 million tons of coal per year.

To obtain the coal necessary for this gigantic operation, New England Electric has commissioned the first coal fired, coal carrying ship to be built in the United States in 25 years. It is being built by General Dynamics shipyard in Quincy, Massachusetts at a cost of $60 million and will enter service in 1983. When in service, it will bring coal from eastern fields

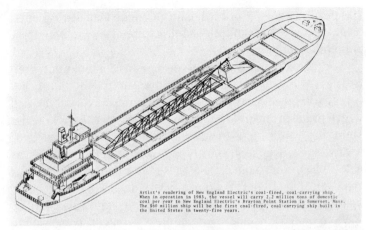

Artist's rendering of New England Electric's coal-fired, coal-carrying ship. When in operation in 1983, the vessel will carry 2.2 million tons of domestic coal per year to New England Electric's Brayton Point Station in Somerset, Mass. The $60 million ship will be the first coal-fired, coal-carrying ship built in the United States in twenty-five years.

Fig. 18-4. Artist's rendering of New England Electric's coal-fired, coal-carrying ship. When in operation in 1983, the vessel will carry 2.2 million tons of domestic coal per year to New England Electric's Brayton Point Station in Somerset, Mass. The $60 million ship will be the first coal-fired, coal-carrying ship built in the United States in twenty-five years (courtesy New England Electric System).

from railheads at Hampton Roads, Baltimore and Philadelphia. It will deliver coal at $55 a ton to New England, and as soon as it can, New England Electric wants to convert one of its units at the South Street Station in Providence, Rhode Island, as well as the Western Massachusetts Electric Company's station at Mt. Tom, just above Holyoke on the Connecticut River (see Figs. 18-4 and 18-5).

Best of all, according to New England Electric, atmospheric pollution will actually be lessened in its switch from oil to coal. It is installing electrostatic precipitators.

OLDER TECHNOLOGIES FOR CLEANING COAL'S COMBUSTION

As the use of coal has increased dramatically during the 70s, attention has been focused more and more on its effects on the atmosphere. A valuable article by Charles Komanoff appeared in the September 1980 Journal of the Air Pollution Control Association on the costs and accomplishments of present air-pollution control technologies. Electrostatic stack scrubbers and precipitators add greatly to the cost of conventional coal fired plants. Though plants so equipped which will come on line in the late 80s will cost approximately

221

130 percent more (not including inflation) than 1971 plants, plants using the scrubbers and precipitators will give off 91 percent less pollutants.

After examining the various options for pollution control, Komanoff also believes the pressurized fluidized bed combustion system, developed by American Electric Power offers great promise for the next several decades. Yet, despite this cost, coal fired power is still cheaper than nuclear, according to Komanoff's analysis. Back in 1978, when I was able to have Mr. Komanoff address the Board of Trustees of the Vermont Electric Cooperative, he showed projected costs of nuclear versus coal fired power in New York State by 1985 to be 8.1¢ for a kilowatt of nuclear power, compared to 5.0¢ a kilowatt for coal fired power. The reasons for the difference were; 1. capital costs, $1875/kW for nuclear, versus $1025/kW for coal, and 2. the lower capacity factor of nuclear plants: 55 percent, versus an average 70 percent for coal fired ones. Unfortunately, his advice was not heeded. Although I voted in the negative, the majority voted that the Co-op should invest in several nuclear plants projected for New England. Just the other day, the Boston Edison Company announced that it would cancel its Pilgrim II reactor. The WSJ story indicated Boston Edison's share of the loss would be $291 million. The Vermont Electric Co-op, owning but 0.2% had a much smaller loss. According to the Co-op's annual report, issued in June, 1981, its investment in Pilgrim II is $822,427. While some of this loss may be made up by the sale of hardware already bought but not yet installed, the rest of it must be passed on to Co-op members/users who will also have to pay for other generating facilities as well.

BUT COAL IS DIRTY AND HARMS AIR QUALITY

In March 1980, a Presidential Commission, appointed by President Carter after the 110 day coal strike in 1978 reported: "The accelerated construction of new coal plants would not harm the environment, would not require any softening of antipollution regulations and, in the long run, would not increase the cost of electricity and industrial energy."

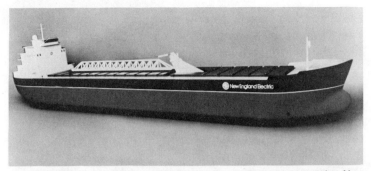

Fig. 18-5. This coal fired ship will enter service in 1983, to bring coal to New England Electric System's coal fired plants in New England from coal ports in Virginia (Norfolk), Maryland (Baltimore), and Pennsylvania (Philadelphia) (courtesy of New England Electric System).

Three years before, a committee of the National Academy of Sciences warned however of global climate changes, if the burning of coal, oil, and natural gas continued to spew carbon dioxide into the atmosphere. As the amount of CO_2 increases, ocean water will gradually warm, and by the middle of the next century, significant changes will occur. Sea levels will rise as a result of the melting of the polar ice cap, rainfall patterns will change, and there will be changes in agricultural zones and desert areas.

Dire predictions indeed! However, the study stopped short of a recommendation of a slowdown in the use of coal. Indeed, "the committee's chairman, Roger Revelle, of both Harvard and the University of California at San Diego, said; . . . In my opinion it is perfectly all right to use coal the next few decades provided we don't get committed to it. But he added; "We have to be prepared to go to sources other than coal within 50 years!" (WSJ 7/25/77)

CAN COAL SERVE AS THE HOPED FOR BRIDGE FUEL FOR THE NEXT TWO DECADES?

Given its handicaps, and given modern technologies for cleaning its combustion, the question persists: can the world safely burn coal now until newer, renewable technologies come on line? Elliot Cutler, former Associate Director, Office of Management and Budget for Natural Resources, Energy and Science, in the Carter Administration, terms coal just this: the "energy bridge" for the next twenty or thirty years. Until the emerging technologies for solar power, voltaic solar cells are made economically so as to be competitive, until micro and macro hydropower, as outlined previously, are developed, until wind research makes it economical, until we learn more about conservation and co-generation, he believes that coal will be the fuel of the next decades, the bridge to the 21st century's energy needs.

Because of this, he predicts coal demand will triple by the year 2000. The United States has nearly 30 percent of the world's economically recoverable coal reserves, and will see its coal export trade expand four fold, from 90 million tons a year to 350 million tons annually by the end of the century. The recent world coal study, Mr. Cutler points out, says that coal trade with Japan and the developing countries of Southeast Asia, which presently accounts for but 3 percent of the total world coal trade, could within 20 years make up 40 percent of the world coal trade. This will be 10 to 15 times greater than it is today.

But America needs better harbors for deeper draft shipping and better railroads for inland transportation of coal. Mr. Cutler sums up his belief: "We have the opportunity to help build the energy bridge that can assure a stable, growing economy for ourselves and for other nations. It is important to us and to the world that we seize that opportunity."

Chapter 19

Solar Power's Bright Promise

Everyone is familiar with passive solar energy systems: roof-top collectors for home heating, solar hot water systems, solar heated greenhouses, almost every form of low temperature heat needed by man. Some are not so familiar with other energy systems which can properly be classed as solar. Solar is anything which depends on the sun for its action. Thus, hydro is a form of solar, biomass conversion, wind, garbage and refuse burning, anything which results from the action of the sun. Fossil fuels of course did come from the sun millions of years ago. For the purposes of this chapter, we shall define solar energy as that which results from the direct use of solar energy, first in passive systems, then in the direct conversion of sunlight to electricity.

Several years ago, the Massachusetts Institute of Technology developed a much improved passive solar system for home heating. In an experimental building these scientists used special one inch thick ceiling panels filled with a newly developed chemical that prevents daytime temperatures from rising above 73 degrees, and stores excess heat from the daytime, for use at night. Moreover, these materials designed by MIT add but 5 percent to the construction cost of a house. Timothy Johnson, research associate in charge of this project said that this design would keep a house warm for 48 hours without sun during the heating season.

The building used a new transparent plastic material placed between two sheets of glass, which makes such windows four times more effective in retaining heat than conventional insulated glass ones.

This past June, the Wall Street Journal reported the first solar electric home in the nation, built in Carlisle, Massachusetts. Designed by MIT's Lincoln Laboratory, on a sunny afternoon, this house generates 7.5 kW, more than enough to supply its needs. Although such a house is yet only a plaything for the rich, its builder felt confident that it would sell. Using all the passive solar devices so far designed, the electrical requirements of the house are kept to a minimum. For auxiliary heat on cold winter nights, it uses a wood stove, as well as a heat pump that can draw heat from water which is above 32 degrees F.

THE BEVERLY HIGH SCHOOL PROJECT

A much more ambitious project, funded by a grant from the Department of Energy, was the 100 kilowatt Beverly High School Photovoltaic Project, one of the first large-scale solar electric systems in the United States. The project, costing $2.7 million, makes the cost per kilowatt of installed capacity prohibitive, at $27,000 a kilowatt. Participants in the project were Solar Power Corporation, an affiliate of Exxon Corporation, the prime contractor; Massachusetts Electric Company, subsidiary of New England Electric System; Stone and Webster Engineering Corporation, and the Beverly High School System.

The solar array of more than 3,200 solar modules is installed on the southerly facing hill behind the building's north side (see Fig. 19-1).

GEORGETOWN UNIVERSITY'S SOLAR PROJECT

Last summer, in my visit to Georgetown University's atmospheric fluidized bed coal co-generating facility, I saw its new 300 kilowatt solar project, also funded by the Depart-

Fig. 19-1. The Beverly High School photovoltaic project (courtesy New England Electric System).

ment of Energy. Again the cost of this project was high, $20,000 a peak kilowatt.

The importance of such projects as Georgetown's and Beverly High School's is that they are experimental precursors to large scale application of solar cell technology. When American Astronauts first landed on the moon they had photovoltaic cells which did just what the cells on the layered roof of Georgetown's building, or the hillside installation at Beverly are doing: they generated electricity directly from the sun. Since that day, inventors all over the nation have been hard at work to produce cells efficient enough to compete with present day generation techniques for the mass production of electricity.

Many people put off the day for this innovative technology until the 21st century. Many remember the television commercial, sponsoring one of the Sunday noon talk shows. An engineer is explaining how a grade crossing warning light is being operated by a solar cell. Unfortunately, he tells his high school audience, solar cell technology will only account for but four percent of our electric generation even by the year 2000. Now it begins to appear that the great day for massive amounts of solar generated electricity is closer than many thought possible.

Several years ago, weird stories of satellites in space, high above the clouds were titillating the imagination of the populace. These satellites would send laser beams to converge on the target chamber at Los Alamos Laboratory. This almost science fiction scenario was being developed for nuclear fusion technology. Other scientists however, turned their attention to developing more efficient photovoltaic solar cells. Four years ago, in 1977, Stanford Ovshinsky made headlines with his announcement that his Energy Conversion Devices Co. of Troy, Michigan, had developed chemical modifications to the amorphous semiconductors he pioneered in the 1960s. These amorphous silicon semiconductors can be manufactured much cheaper than the crystalline silicon solar cells which preceded them.

Early in 1981, Ovshinsky reported an efficiency of 6.6 percent for his cells, as compared with 5.5 percent achieved by researchers at RCA in 1977. Ovshinsky hoped to achieve a 10 percent efficiency which when achieved, would make such solar generated electricity competitive with conventional forms of fuel generated power.

But Mr. Ovshinsky was not working alone. The new solar cell is being developed under an agreement with Atlantic Richfield Co., which put up $28.3 million for his (Ovshinsky's) research.

Indeed, big oil just as it has pushed into coal, and nuclear power, is now pushing its way into the burgeoning development of solar electric power. Last May, Mr. Ovshinsky made headlines again by announcing he had developed a device that could produce electricity directly from sunlight at a cost equal to or less than that of making electricity from coal, oil or atomic energy. He predicted that his little company Energy Conversion Devices, could be in pilot plant production of power-producing rooftop panels within three years. The only thing stopping him, according to this story in May, was financing.

By July however, this hurdle had apparently been overcome. Standard Oil of Ohio (Sohio) had agreed to form a partnership with him that could provide up to $80 million more over the next three years to develop Energy Conversion's solar technology. After 12 to 18 months of development, Sohio has the option of swapping its present investment into a maximum of 600,000 Energy Conversion Devices shares, about 17 percent of the company. The second partnership that will be formed will result in ECD's owning 51% and Sohio 49%.

To the outsider, such agreements are rather complex and confusing, in light of Mr. Ovshinsky's prior alliance with Atlantic Richfield. However, Energy Conversion said, "its current agreements" with Sohio "are fully compatible" with the "earlier one involving Atlantic Richfield."

With such financial backing, one must believe Ovshinsky is on to something. The Wall Street Journal reported: "The general consensus is that thin-film solar cells will be the cells of the future," said T.W. Fraser Russell, director of the Energy Conversion Institute at the University of Delaware. "Only thin films, rather than solid crystals can be manufactured in quantities adequate to cover the acreage needed for solar-energy use, he explains."

The Journal continued to quote Mr. Russell: "There are only two thin films in the advanced stages of development, . . . One is Mr. Ovshinsky's, composed of an alloy of amorphous silicon, hydrogen and fluorine. The other is a solar cell developed by the Delaware institute, using layers of cadmium sulphide and copper sulphide laid down on a sheet of copper."

Whether Mr. Russell is correct in his assessment of this process or not, one may say with certainty, it appears that we are in the fullness of time for simultaneous inventions in this field of direct solar electricity.

In May, 1981, a UPI dispatch talked of the rapidity of developments in Europe and America. These researchers are not only looking for the production of electricity, but how to use that electricity to produce hydrogen for fuel that will displace gasoline in internal combustion engines. To that end, this story told of the huge Italian Montedison Co. It is working with Swiss scientists, and has developed a process, using solar heat to produce hydrogen from water in commercially feasible quantity and cost.

Last year, Eugene R. Anderson of Willis Point, Texas, announced he had a process to generate hydrogen produced continuously from water in the vehicle by chemical reaction without the application of any external energy. Far fetched? Yet, Anderson told UPI, "that successful independent laboratory tests on his invention now had been carried out in Britain and he expects to announce licensing agreements soon."

CONSUMERS SOLAR ELECTRIC POWER

Another small firm claiming to have cracked the secret of manufacturing a voltaic solar cell of high efficiency, that is, from 15 to 18 percent, compared to the 6 percent of the moonshots, is struggling to get attention. Based in Culver City California it believes its gallium arsenide solar cell to be more advanced than any other. At its solar farm in Arizona it uses the solar electricity with a catalyst to obtain hydrogen by electrolysis. From this, it claims to have an automotive fuel, essentially hydrogen in the form of ammonia which it says can be manufactured for 60¢ a gallon, and can be used in present cars with but little conversion.

Claiming harassment from Big Oil, this company has resorted to the strategy of holding its voting class A stock closely, among three officers of the company, so as to preclude a takeover. That this is no idle fear, is shown by the Wall Street Journal's reporting that Exxon owns 100 percent of Solar Technology International, Inc., as well as SES Inc. The Journal told of Mobil's owning 80 percent of Mobil-Tyco Solar Energy Corporation, and Standard Oil of Indiana's owning 25 percent of Solarex Corporation. Phillips Petroleum owns 30 percent of Acurex Corporation.

BIG OIL'S TAKEOVER OF SOLAR POWER

According to the American Petroleum Institute, oil companies directly or indirectly control 77 percent of the sales made by the solar electric industry. Government officials say the oil industry's share is closer to 90 percent. Three years ago, oil companies had less than 50 percent of the market.

One disturbing aspect of this control of the emerging solar electric industry by big oil is: solar companies backed by big oil have far more clout in obtaining government subsidies.

In 1979, small business received but 15 percent of the $150 million solar budget. Big business obtained 45 percent, with the rest going to universities and government laboratories.

One official of a small solar firm in Massachusetts, Solector-Thermo, Inc., of Dracut said that although his company was 5 years ahead of the rest of the industry, its request for government funds was turned down repeatedly. Even so, this company has fought off takeover bids from ARCO as well as others.

A Wall Street Journal Article concluded: "At least one DOE official admits a bias toward big companies when it comes to solar power . . . DOE's director of solar electricity says: 'it's difficult to do business with small firms because they lack sizable staffs and sophistication in presenting proposals.'"

As in the early days of the automobile, hundreds of small companies eventually disappeared, so too in solar-electric cell development, it is probable, there will be but few large survivors. Yet in this crucial research and development stage, the cross-fertilization of ideas from many companies working on the problem is most valuable.

Early in 1980, there was a newspaper report that scientists at California's Institute of Technology had found a catalyst to speed up the electrolysis of water into its components, hydrogen and oxygen. After all, Germany fought most of World War II without access to natural petroleum, powering its war machine with synthetic fuel. Hydrogen is among the most explosive of elements, and one of the most abundant on earth. Four fifths of the earth's surface is covered by water, whose chemical composition is simply H_2O. These men at Caltech are now looking for a longer lasting catalyst and less expensive than rhodium which is very efficient. Presently their search has turned toward tungsten and molybdenum.

Whatever the validity of these various claims, it is apparent that much technical progress has been made. It is no wonder that the National Aeronautics and Space Agency optimistically predicts that solar power can provide all the electricity needed in the United States by 1986. A United Press International dispatch, from Cleveland, reported that solar electricity would be commercially competitive with other forms of generation within six years. The story continued: "In addition, there is enough space on south-facing roofs across the U.S. for solar cells to supply the nation's entire electrical energy needs." This statement was attributed to Dr. Robert R. Farber, manager of Solar Photovoltaics Technology at NASA's Jet Propulsion Laboratory in Pasadena, California.

Dr. Farber predicted that solar electricity will cost 5 to 9 cents a kilowatt hour. Farber summed up: "By 1986 the average homeowner could have a 5 kW solar unit installed on his roof for as low as $3,500, taking tax credit incentives into account."

One problem the story did not address was: how to overcome the lack of electric generation at night. This of course could be overcome by a battery bank, or interconnecting with one's utility which would provide baseload power when the sun was not shining. Possibly surplus daytime electricity could be used to fill the top reservoir of a pumped storage facility, to come on line at night.

Such solar speculation is all but mind boggling. Whether it comes to pass or not, depends on technologies not yet in place. Yet, stable, established utilities such as Southern California Edison Company, whose interest in nuclear fission reactors is well known, seem to believe it will come to pass. Last October 20, (1980) Southern Cal. Edison startled the utility world by announcing that it expected to use alternative energy systems for 30 percent of its expected growth by 1990. After steadfastly maintaining for years that such things as solar, geothermal, wind and hydro, could not possibly account for more than 10 percent of its energy requirements by 1990, it suddenly changed course. In the next decade, its estimates from wind power have tripled, and its solar projections have gone from zero to 310 megawatts.

Chapter 20

Wood, Wind, Waste
and Other Technologies

While many large sawmills and papermills have used bark, sawdust, slabs, scrap of all kinds to fuel boilers which co-generate a large part of their power, plans for large scale utility wood-fired plants have run into difficulty, both in North Carolina and in Vermont. Burlington's municipal electric department is still trying to find an economical and environmentally acceptable way to bring its projected 50 megawatt wood fired plant on line.

WOOD

Wood of course is used in the great majority of Vermont homes either to heat them entirely, or to supplement other systems. Some question the environmental effects of wood smoke. There was a derogatory story in the Wall Street Journal a while back about the narrow valley where Waterbury, Vermont lies, suffering from excess wood smoke pollution.

Whether wood smoke is carcinogenic or not is an open question. At the turn of the century, all Vermont homes were heated with wood. Nothing was heard then of adverse effects. Whether this was due to ignorance, or the fact that wood smoke is "softer" than other pollutants I do not know. This I do know: the fragrance coming from a wood fired sugar evaporator is far superior to that from an oil fired rig. When my wood stove is keeping me cozy in 30 below weather, and I step outside for a moment, the fragrance emanating from the chimney is pleasing to the nostrils, and not offensive as the acrid stench from the oil burner.

One friend in Hadley, Massachusetts, less than an hour's drive from my home, is President of the Montgomery Rose Co. He recently converted the heating of his acres of greenhouses to wood chips, with a savings in the neighborhood of 400 percent over oil.

Whether wood becomes acceptable as a boiler fuel for electric utilities will depend on the answers to questions as to its environmental acceptability, whether "clear cutting" will be tolerated, with its threat to the soil and erosion, whether other alternatives such as coal are available until the new power sources of the 21st century are commercially viable.

WIND POWER

The first commercial application of wind power by a utility occurred in Vermont during World War II. On a small mountain top west of Rutland, Grandpa's Knob, this giant windmill with a wing span of 175 feet pumped 1250 kilowatts of power into the Central Vermont Public Service Company's lines. It worked for two years. Then one of its blades blew off and that was the end of it. The cost of this installation came to $190 a kilowatt of installed capacity. Other forms of generating equipment cost but $125 a kilowatt at that time. Hence the project was abandoned.

On January 21, 1981 the National Aeronautics and Space Agency began the operation of the Nation's first wind farm, with 7,500 kilowatts capacity near Goldendale, Washington. Between these two events the energy picture confronting the world has literally been turned on its head.

In the present energy crunch many folk are again turning to windmills, not the kind that dotted the country before the days of the Rural Electric Administration in the 1930s, but new ones with improved design, not just for pumping water but for supplying electric power are popping up everywhere there is sufficient wind to turn their blades. One book that gives a complete rundown of the kinds of wind systems and equipment available is George Sullivan's, *Wind Power*. These systems are usually cheaper than hydro systems to install. Their dependability depends on the vagaries of the wind, which is even more uncertain than the vagaries of climate and precipitation.

In August, 1976, the Energy Research and Development Administration built an experimental 1500 kilowatt wind turbine and generator in Ohio. Unfortunately, ERDA's effort met the same fate as befell the windmill atop Grandpa's Knob. Another wind machine, built by the Hamilton Standard Propeller Division of United Technologies, with General Electric supplying the electrical components was placed in service on a mountain near Boone, North Carolina.

Presently, the Department of Energy has five wind turbines ranging in size from 200 to 2500 kilowatts in operation. With a grant from the Department of Energy, the Vermont Electric Cooperative is now conducting wind studies atop 3900 foot Stratton Mountain in Southern Vermont, to determine the feasibility of wind generation there. Using a helicopter to install the tower in the fall of 1980, the anemometer was giving good readings until one winter storm came along and blew it away. It would only gauge winds up to 100 miles an hour. See Fig. 20-1. A new wind gauge with a clutch has now been installed, so that after velocities of 100 miles an hour are reached, the instrument will be protected by the clutch disengaging the propeller.

Perhaps the foremost advocate of wind energy in the nation is a retired naval officer, now a Professor of Engineering at the University of Massachusetts. William Heronimus advocates a string of windmills in the Atlantic mounted on Texas Tower like structures. From his naval experience he knows the winds blow almost continuously off the New England coast. His proposal showed that New England could supply four times its electrical needs from wind power at an initial cost far less than the nuclear alternative. Additionally, his scheme envisaged using the surplus electricity to produce hydrogen from seawater, which then could be burned either for boiler fuel, or to power automobiles without the noxious pollutants internal combustion engines now spew into the atmosphere.

Professor Heronimus had another idea. From his knowledge of the sea, he saw the temperature gradients between the various levels of seawater. These too, he stoutly maintains can produce energy. It is indeed unfortunate that such creative minds as his are not heeded in America's present search for energy. Before the advent of rural electrification, an estimated 6 million windmills were made and sold in the United States between 1850 and the early 1900s.

Five years ago, the program manager of the National Aeronautical and Space Agency's office of wind power predicted that wind energy could provide 5 to 10 percent of the nation's energy needs at its maximum efficiency and usage. Whether even this most modest estimate is attained, or whether Professor Heronimous' far more grandiose scheme is adopted, seems dim. The Department of Energy's enthusiasm for wind energy at best seemed to be modest. At its most optimistic point, it had only 35 study grants outstanding. From these, it expected to select five for demonstration projects. Now even that has "gone with the wind."

Federal subsidies for research and development of wind energy have now been deleted from the Federal budget. Commenting on the situation, the Congressional Research Service of the Library of Congress said: "The current cost of wind-generated electricity is 15 to 30 cents per kilowatt hour (kWh). This figure compares with a current 4 cents per kWh cost of electricity from newly constructed coal-fired powerplants. DOE's goal is to reduce wind costs to the 4 to 8 cents per kWh range by 1985, the 3 to 5 cents range by 1990, and the 3 to 4 cents range by 2000. Cost reductions are expected to be achieved through mass production and technological improvement."

But now, wind energy is cut out of the Reagan budget, and it is questionable whether the very small wind energy companies, presently about 50 in number can survive. The largest, according to this Library of Congress study, is Enertech of Norwich, Vermont, which has a production line of just 60 units a month.

Fig. 20-1. The Vermont Electric Cooperative's Wind Energy Tower atop Stratton Mountain in southern Vermont. Because of the Department of Energy's termination of wind energy research, this project has now been abandoned (photo by Allan Gill, courtesy, Co-op Life).

The Electric Power Research Institute reported that in 1979, 50 utilities were involved with 83 wind energy projects. "Several projects," the research report of the Library of Congress says, "involved WECS (Wind Energy Conversion Systems) developed without Federal assistance—a possible indication of the private sector's growing interest in wind energy technology. In the most notable effort, Southern

California Edison at Rosemead, California, is installing a 3,000 kW unit on its grid with the possible acquisition of 40 more units. Several other utilities have purchased 300 kW and 500 kW units for integration with existing grids. Hawaii Electric plans to install six 500 kW units in a "wind farm" project, and may purchase additional units for an eventual 80 megawatts of installed WECS capacity.

For those interested in obtaining a list of wind energy conversion system manufacturers, Rockwell International, Energy Systems Group, Wind Systems Program, has compiled a list of some 40 U.S. manufacturers of small electrical wind machines in business as of April 15,1980. Its address is: Rock Flats Plant, PO Box 484, Golden, Colorado 80401.

WASTE: ELECTRICITY FROM TRASH

New England Power, a subsidiary of the New England Electric System has signed two contracts with a subsidiary of UOP Company, Inc. (formerly Universal Oil Products Co.) to generate electricity from trash. One is a project in Lawrence and Haverhill, Massachusetts, initially to use 1500 tons of municipal waste daily, but capable of expansion to 3,000 tons of solid waste each day. The other is for a similar project at North Andover, Massachusetts. Both are part of New England Power's "Neesplan", with a target of obtaining 200 megawatts of generation from alternate energy sources.

UOP, a world wide high technology company has similar, yet larger projects (as well as smaller) both in the United States and Europe. Chicago has processed a significant part of its solid waste since 1970. Another project in Harrisburg, Pennsylvania uses 720 tons a day.

In France, the Plant at *Paris/Ivry,* the largest such installation, burns 2,650 tons per day. Other plants in England, Japan, Switzerland, Munich, and West Germany use municipal waste, not only solving communities' solid waste disposal problems, but recovering valuable metals as well as generating significant amounts of power. Operation of such facilities is virtually odorless, dustless, and noiseless.

UOP, in a long term cooperative agreement with Josef Martin Feuerungsbau GmbH (Matin) of West Germany, an international engineering company with more than 50 years experience in solid waste combustion and steam generation, is interested in 87 such solid waste plants in operation or under construction in 15 countries.

Several years ago, Boston Edison signed a $100 million contract with Wheelabrator-Frye of Hampton, New Hampshire for a similar trash burning, generating plant for its system. Wheelabrator-Frye is also building a trash plant in Peekskill, New York, at a cost of $165 million with construction to begin in 1984. When completed, this will be the largest of its kind in the U.S. The plant will operate at close to 2,500 degrees Fahrenheit, and will eliminate everything with the exception of ferrous metals that will be sold for scrap and certain other metal residue which is used for paving roads. Consolidated Edison, New York City, is expected to be the major purchaser of the power produced by this plant. Under 20 year contracts, a minimum commitment of 350,000 tons of garbage has already been made to the plant.

In 1977, the Westchester County Hospital, Valhalla, New York, attempted to enter into a similar contract with Wheelabrator-Frye but the project was blocked because of its location. A smaller project at Saugus, Massachusetts sells its steam to a nearby General Electric plant to generate electricity. According to Wheelabrator-Frye, this plant has been profitable since 1979.

Similarly the Foster Wheeler Company avers that the refuse fired steam generator is an excellent means of converting from oil, gas, and coal, and producing substantial amounts of steam for co-generation. It is simply making something out of nothing—nothing that is, but a by-product of civilization which has been an increasingly perplexing problem as to how to handle it. Instead of polluting the ocean by dumping refuse out to sea, only to have it wash up on the nearby coastline, cities such as New York, facing the dual problem of waste disposal and no more garbage dumps, will find this method a useful way to conserve energy, save the environment, and at the same time generate by-product steam and electricity. Starting out in 1930, with its first refuse wood fired boiler in Liverpool, Nova Scotia, during the decade of the 1970s, Foster Wheeler received orders for over two dozen refuse wood fired units.

In addition to these installations, in 1945, Foster Wheeler installed the first sugar cane refuse fired boiler in Equador at Valdez. Five additional ones have been added to this, and in Hawaii, Foster Wheeler Kauai, Inc. has under construction another unit which will be part of a 20 megawatt power plant. And again, this unit provides both steam for sugar cane processing as well as the generation of electricity.

A recent study at Harvard's School of Business Administration reports that co-generation can reduce by as much as 50 percent the fuel needed to generate the same amounts of steam and electricity at separate plants.

NUCLEAR FUSION

Though nuclear fusion promises great things for the future, its technology still has to be developed. Nuclear fusion differs from nuclear fission in several important respects. It makes use of the energy released when two atoms are fused together. Fission is the splitting of atoms. Unlike fission, fusion does not produce the toxic by-products such as plutonium that fission reactors produce. Unlike fission, nuclear fusion makes use of light elements, such as hydrogen, whereas nuclear fission uses heavy metallic elements at the other end of the atomic scale. Fusion uses the commonest substance found: water. Fission depends on relatively scarce uranium.

Nations all over the world are working on a nuclear fusion reactor. The United States has committed $20 billion over the next twenty years for fusion research. This is principally being conducted at Princeton University, and the Lawrence Livermore Laboratory in California. Princeton announced a year ago it had made great strides in its work. The problem is: how to achieve sufficiently high temperatures to cause fusion, and in that high temperature to find a metal capable of withstanding heat in the realm of 100 million degrees centigrade inside the fusion vessel.

Two aspects of nuclear fusion make it most appealing to an energy starved world. 1. It makes use of one of the most common elements found on earth, hydrogen. Four fifths of the earth's surface is water, and its primary chemical composition is H_2O, or two atoms of hydrogen for one of oxygen. Whatever else happens on earth, fuel for such a reactor will never be used up. 2. Fusion does nót release nearly the amount of radioactive waste poisons or pose the problem of waste cleanup fission reactors do. The primary radioactive material created by nuclear fission is cobalt 60, which has a half life of 5 years. Of course, everything that is irradiated with high energy particles does become radioactive, and a concrete shield must be built around fusion reactors also. But the staggering waste problem that plagues fission reactors does not exist.

When one realizes that 1 milligram of plutonium constitutes a toxic dose for humans, and that a 600 megawatt fission reactor every two weeks produces enough plutonium to make an atomic bomb, he understands that the world desperately needs an energy source which does not pose such threats to life and peace.

Fusion involves charged particles which cannot move through solids. Fusion therefore must rely on a medium, or plasma, in which fusion takes place. This plasma is a hot gas—composed only of ions and electrons, in which the constituent particles can collide and fuse. To achieve 100 million degrees centigrade necessary to make this fusion process work, scientists have turned to magnetic compression, a process in which Princeton has reported good progress.

Another approach is through laser fusion. Dr. Jay Hirshfield, Yale's specialist in plasma physics writes: "A small pellet of high density gas would be compressed by a factor of 10,000 to the density of the center of a star for only a few billionths of a second. This may require a laser several thousand times more powerful than any now in existence."

Presently, nuclear fusion research is probably about at the same stage as nuclear fission was when Enrico Fermi built the first fission reactor in Chicago in 1942.

In sum, the problem confronting fusion technology is: how to build a reactor in which the hottest substance on earth, plasma, must be surrounded by perhaps the coldest, a superconducting magnet. Scientists hope to be able to solve this riddle and bring the first fusion reactor on line by the end of the 20th century.

SUMMARY

America has several viable options for solving its energy crisis with renewable, non-polluting sources. The technology for vastly increased hydroelectric production is readily available. The technology for large scale generation of solar and wind-powered electricity lies just around the corner. Many firms are working on biomass, garbage, and organic wastes as new sources of electric generation. Until nuclear fusion becomes a reality, hopefully by the year 2,000, coal can serve as a bridge for our present energy requirements, so long as we conserve and do not waste.

Appendices

Appendix A

Centrifugal Pumps as Hydraulic Turbines for the Small Hydropower Market

prepared by
L. SHAFER
MARKETING MANAGER, HYDRO POWER

A. AGOSTINELLI
DIRECTOR OF PRODUCT PLANNING

WORTHINGTON GROUP
McGRAW-EDISON COMPANY

Taneytown, MD 21787

INTRODUCTION

Increasing energy costs have stimulated interest in using available water resources to drive hydraulic turbines. These range from mammoth projects harnessing the tides and flow of major rivers and elevated lakes to very small applications by private individuals with a stream crossing their property. Increasing interest in hydropower is being generated from established consulting engineering firms, newly organized small hydropower companies, the U.S. Corps. of Engineers, private individuals, municipalities and various industrial enterprises.

The number of manufacturers of small hydraulic turbines is extremely limited. If the market continues to expand as rapidly as expected, conventional turbine machinery will not be available. The use of pumps running in reverse as turbines is an excellent alternative to conventional turbomachinery, and even offers many unique advantages. Pumps operating in reverse yield good efficiencies as turbines. In order to extend the high

245

efficiency range, multiple pumps of various sizes can be used instead of one large conventional turbine. Pumps are readily available and many sizes are stock items. Also, pumps are several generations ahead of conventional turbines in cost reduction, they are less sophisticated, easier to install and maintain, and simpler to operate. And pumps are available in a broader range of configurations than conventional turbines—wet pit, dry pit, horizontal, vertical, and even submersible to mention a few.

BACKGROUND

Centrifugal pumps from radial flow to the axial flow geometry can be operated in reverse and used as hydraulic turbines. This dual capability is not just happenstance, since turbomachinery theory predicts this capability. Furthermore, because this theory is applicable, a hydraulic turbine follows the same affinity relationships as do centrifugal pumps. Consequently, the performance of a turbine can be predicted accurately from one set of operating conditions to another, and new turbine designs can be "factored" from existing designs.

THE BEHAVIOR OF PUMPS RUNNING AS TURBINES

Over the years Worthington has tested many pumps as turbines. From these tests we have observed that, when a pump operates as a turbine:
- —Its mechanical operation is smooth and quiet.
- —The peak efficiency as a turbine is essentially the same as its peak efficiency as a pump.
- —The head and flow at the best efficiency point as a turbine are higher than they are as a pump at its best efficiency point.
- —The power output of the turbine at its best efficiency point is higher than the pump input power at its best efficiency point.

TYPICAL PERFORMANCE CHARACTERISTICS

A comparison of the characteristics of normal pump operation with the characteristics of the same pump operated as turbine at the same speed are shown in Figure 1. The curves are normalized by the values of head, flow, efficiency and power at the pump BEP. As mentioned previously, note that the location of the turbine BEP is at a higher flow and head than the pump BEP. The ratio of the turbine capacity and head at BEP to the pump capacity and head at BEP has been observed to vary with specific speed—ratios of 1.1 to 2.2 having been determined by test.

There are two other important characteristics of pumps operating as turbines shown in Figure 1. The first of these is that the turbine maximum efficiencies tend to occur over a wide range of capacity. Consequently, relatively wider ranges of turbine operating head can be accommodated without too adverse an effect upon efficiency.

Secondly, note that there is a value of head at which the turbine power output is zero even though there is flow through the unit (this point is called

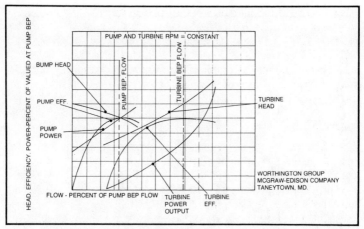

Fig. 1. Normalized performance characteristics for a pump operating in the normal pump mode and in the turbine mode.

the runaway speed). Further reduction in head below this value causes the turbine to begin absorbing power assuming the connected load is capable of providing that power. The flow corresponding to the head at zero power varies from about forty to eighty percent of the flow at turbine BEP, depending upon specific speed.

The turbine performance or rating curve normally supplied to a customer is either the one shown in Figure 2 or 3, whatever his preference. Figure 2 is a plot at constant speed with capacity as abscissa, while Figure 3 is a plot at constant head with speed as abscissa. Given the performance test in either format, the other can easily be obtained by use of the affinity relationships.

Note that the runaway speed can be read directly from the curves of Figure 3. The runaway speed could also be calculated using Figure 2 and the affinity laws, i.e., by taking the product of the value of speed and the square root of the ratio of the head for which runaway needs to be determined to the head at zero power output.

As the foregoing illustrates, the magnitude of the runaway speed can easily be determined for any operating condition provided its value is known for a given condition. This is important data because the magnitude of the runaway speed could affect the structural integrity of the rotating equipment, making it necessary to incorporate overspeed protection in the control system.

CAVITATION

Just as in a pump, at any point in the machine where the local pressure drops to the vapor pressure of the liquid, vapor is formed and cavitation damage can occur. Sufficient outlet or backpressure must be maintained to prevent cavitation just as adequate suction pressure must be maintained on a pump. The value of the available backpressure is called "TAEH" (Total Available

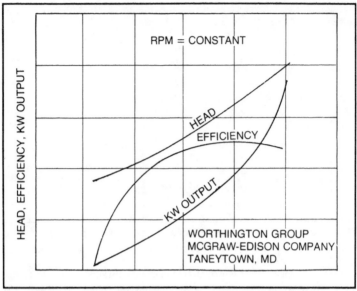

Fig. 2. Typical turbine performance curve for constant speed operation.

Exhaust Head) and the value of the backpressure required for proper turbine operation is called "TREH" (Total Required Exhaust Head).

DESIGN CHANGES

In most instances no design changes or modification need to be made for a pump operating as a turbine. When a selection is made a design review

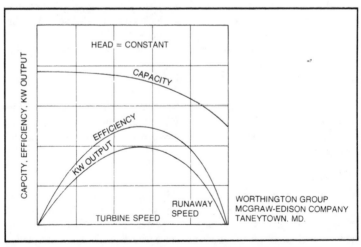

Fig. 3. Typical turbine performance curve for constant head operation.

is required, however, because when operating as a turbine the rotation is reversed and operating heads and power output are generally higher. Consequently, a design review would include items such as:

—Checking that threaded shaft components cannot loosen.
—Evaluating the adequacy of the bearing design.
—Shaft stress analysis.
—Checking the effect of increased pressure forces.

DRAFT TUBES

For high-head turbines, the energy remaining at the outlet is normally very small in relation to the total energy and no pronounced affect on efficiency will occur. However, for low head applications it is important to minimize the remaining energy after exit from the runner in order to keep the efficiency high. Consequently, specially designed diffusers and draft tubes may be required at these lower heads when efficiency evaluations are made.

HYDRAULIC TURBINE DATA

Customer Name		Street 5310 Taneytown Pike
Power Plant Location		City - State - Zip PO Box 91 Taneytown, Md. 21787
Customer Inquiry	Customer Order	Quotation No. Date

CONDITIONS OF SERVICE

	RATED	MAXIMUM	MINIMUM
INLET HEAD - FEET			
EXHAUST HEAD - FEET			
NET TURBINE HEAD - FEET			
CAPACITY (CFS OR GPM)			
TOT. AVAIL. EXHAUST HEAD - FEET			
NOMINAL SPEED - RPM			
WATER QUALITY			

TURBINE

☐ WET PIT   ☐ DRY PIT   ☐ VERTICAL SHAFT   ☐ HORIZONTAL SHAFT

CONSTRUCTION (Special materials, critical dimensions, etc.)

DRIVEN EQUIPMENT

GENERATOR   ☐ INDUCTION   ☐ SYNCHRONOUS ☐ OTHER:
ENCLOSURE   ☐ WP-1   ☐ TEFC   ☐ OTHER:
ELECTRICAL PHASE _____ HERTZ _____ VOLTAGE_____ SERVICE FACTOR _____
OTHER DATA: (WP = Weather   (TEFC = Totally
                      Protected.)   Enclosed, Fan Cooled.)

FOR WORTHINGTON USE ONLY

CONVERTED PUMP CONDITIONS AT RATED POINT: FLOW - GPM _____ HEAD - FEET_____

PUMP SELECTION_____

TOT. REQ'D. EXH. HD. - FT. ____ EFFICIENCY_____ % FULL LOAD R.P.M. _____ RUNAWAY R.P.M. _____

SHAFT STRESS-P.S.I. _____ MATERIAL REQ'D. _____

CASING PRESS - P.S.I. _____ MATERIAL REQ'D. _____
OTHER DATA:

249

WORTHINGTON'S COMMITMENT

Worthington is deeply committed to the hydro turbine market. We have a rapidly growing population of successful installations. One such site in "upstate" New York, using a 36 inch pump as a turbine, has been installed and running trouble-free since 1949!

In order to obtain more data on the performance of pumps operating as turbines, Worthington has undertaken an extensive testing program to improve our selection methods. We are also planning to publish technical reports and curves to assist customers with specific applications.

Worthington has the broadest range of pumps available in the industry, including practically every configuration, size, and type needed to meet customers requirements. This vast capability is available to the hydro-power market for turbine applications. Coupled with both the historical experience and modern creativity of our sales, marketing, and engineering personnel, Worthington is in the ideal position to meet the challenges of waterpower development.

Appendix B

Engineering Services

The importance of obtaining a competent engineering consultant can not be overstated. If one does not have any acquaintances who are competent engineers, the following sources may enable him to find one.

The American Public Power Association: 2600 Virginia Ave., N.W., Washington, D.C. 20037, and its regional Public Power Associations publish magazines replete with ads of engineering firms. The Northeast Public Power Association's monthly publication, POWER LINES, 148 Linden Street, Wellesley, Massachusetts 02181, has many such advertisements.

The Northeast Regional Agricultural Engineering Service, an activity of the Cooperative Extension Services of the Northeast Land Grant Universities and the United States Department of Agriculture, with headquarters at Riley-Robb Hall, Cornell University, Ithaca, New York, 14853, is specially geared to small hydro. Its bulletin: Small Hydroelectric Plants, FS 13, may be of value. Its selected bibliographies are also helpful.

The United States Government has a wealth of bibliographic material. Selected U.S. Government Publications, Superintendent of Documents, U.S. Government Printing Office, Washington, D.C. 20402 is a monthly magazine with all available government publications listed. The July 1981 issue, for instance, has 13 entries under Energy: 20 entries under Environment.

Patrick Haynes, Detroit, Maine, 04929 is a qualified engineer particularly interested in small hydro.

Hervey Scudder's Hydro Power Development Center, 67 Main Street, Brattleboro, Vermont, 05301, can give competent technical information and serve on a consulting basis, particularly in New England.

The RE Magazine, the official organ of the more than 1000 rural electric cooperatives comprising the National Rural Electric Cooperative Association in the United States has a wealth of advertisements of engineering firms and consultants. If a copy is not available from one of the local rural cooperatives in your area, the national address is: 1800 Massachusetts Avenue, N.W., Washington, D.C. 20036.

Appendix C

Selected References

Article

"Lowhead System for Generating Power From Water." 1978. R. Wolf. *Organic Gardening and Farming,* 25: 77-8 (June).

Books

Design of Small Dams. 1973. Department of the Interior. Available from U.S. Government Printing Office, Superintendent of Documents, Washington, D. C. 20402.

Financing Hydropower Redevelopment. Proaction Institute, 206 Urban Planning Building, Michigan State University, East Lansing, MI 48824.

Harnessing Water Power for Home Energy. 1978. Dermot McGuigan. Garden Way Publishing Co., Charlotte, VT 05445. $9.95.

Hydropower Redevelopment. Proaction Institute, 206 Urban Planning Building, Michigan State University, East Lansing, MI 48824.

Low-Cost Development of Small Water-Power Sites. 1967. H. W. Hamm. VITA, 3706 Rhode Island Avenue, Mt. Rainier, MD 20822.

Periodical

Small Hydro Bulletin. A collection of news items, activities, and meetings regarding small hydroelectric development. Subscription available from RoseMarie Peterson, Hydropower Programs, Idaho National Engineering Laboratory, P.O. Box 1625, Idaho Falls, ID 83415

Reports

"Fundamental Economic Issues in The Development of Small-Scale Hydro." January 30, 1979. Report DOE/RA-23-216.00.0.0-02. Available from National Technical Information Service, Springfield, VA 22161. $4.50.

"Micro-Hydro Power: Reviewing an Old Concept." Report DOE/ET/01752-1. Available from National Center for Appropriate Technology, P.O. Box 3838, Butte, MT 59071.

"Small Hydroelectric Plants." Report FS-13, Northeast Regional Agricultural Engineering Service, Riley-Robb Hall, Cornell University, Ithaca, NY 14853.

Appendix D

Annotated Bibliography
of DOE Hydropower Reports

FINAL REPORT ON TIDAL POWER STUDY for the United States Energy Research and Development Administration, by W. W. Wayne, Jr., Stone & Webster Engineering Corporation, Boston, Massachusetts, Vol. 1 and Vol. 2. Prepared under contract No. (49-18)-2293 DGE/2283-3, March 1977.

This two-volume report discusses the status and potential of tidal energy as a world power source. It specifically discussed two sites in the United States where tidal power could be utilized.

Research opportunities are considered which could reduce the costs of tidal power stations making them more competitive as a national energy source.

Environmental, societal, and legal consequences (both good and bad) of building a major tidal power plant are listed.

LOW-HEAD/SMALL HYDRO-ELECTRIC WORKSHOP, September 6-9, 1977. At the New England Center for Continuing Education, Durham, New Hampshire, by Louis H. Klotz and Fred K. Manasse, Center for Industrial and Institutional Development, University of New Hampshire, Durham, New Hampshire 03824.

Sponsored by the Energy and Research Development Administration's Division of Geothermal Energy, the Workshop was organized to provide ERDA with guidance for their low-head hydro planning. The Workshop lasted 3-½ days and included 121 participants representing governmental agencies, energy offices, manufacturers, conservation agencies, universities, and legal agencies. Manufacturers from France, Japan, Canada and Austria were also present.

The participants focused on the issues of resource assessment, engineering development, institutional and legal barriers, environmental and safety issues, economics and marketability, and demonstrations. This Report contains extensive coverage of the participants' deliberation on these issues as well as complete coverage of all the Workshop activities. Over ninety specific, as well as generalized, recommendations, responding to the focused issues, are documented from conception to final form.

IDAHO FALLS HYDROELECTRIC PROJECT, UPPER AND LOWER POWER PLANTS, PRELIMINARY REPORTS International Engineering Company, Inc., IDO-10071, February 1978.

This document includes: a brief appraisal of the existing generation facilities and of the condition of the existing concrete structures; a geological reconnaissance of the Upper and Lower Power Plant Sites; analysis of the power potential of the two sites; investigation and comparative evaluation of four alternatives for redeveloping the streamflows for power generation; selection of the most suitable alternative for development; and preparation of drawings and detailed quantity and cost estimates for the recommended development.

IDAHO FALLS CITY HYDROELECTRIC POWER PLANT, PRELIMINARY REPORT, International Engineering Company, Inc., IDO-10073, February 1978.

The document reports the investigation and comparative evaluation of four alternatives for redeveloping the hydroelectric potential of the streamflows at the City Plant; selection of the most suitable redevelopment alternative; and evaluation of the existing environment and the environmental aspects of the recommended development.

REPORT ON TURBOGENERATING EQUIPMENT FOR LOW HEAD HYDROELECTRIC DEVELOPMENTS, by W.K. VerPlanck and W.W. Wayne, Jr., Stone & Webster Engineering Corporation, Boston, Massachusetts, IDO-1962-1, April 1978.

The report summarizes the current status of certain selected turbo-generation equipment suitable for low-head hydroelectric plants. Information from the Stone & Webster Engineering Corporation files was used (particularly for the Rock Island Hydroelectric Project) as well as information from visits to manufacturers laboratories and to other hydroelectric

254

plants. In particular, the following types of hydraulic turbo-generator systems are discussed: Alsthom-Neyrpic bulb turbines, Ossberger cross flow turbines, Escher Wyss Straflo turbines, Barber Mini-Hydel turbine, and Allis-Chalmers' series of standard tube turbines.

SMALL LOW-HEAD HYDROELECTRIC POWER, PROCEEDINGS FROM THE MIDWEST REGIONAL CONFERENCE, May 23-25, 1978, Michigan State University, College of Engineering, East Lansing, Michigan, IDO-10076, August 1978.

The report includes papers covering a wide spectrum of issues surrounding the establishment (or reestablishment of abandoned sites) of small low-head hydroelectric power plants. Topics addressed include: current (under) utilization of hydropower sites, rehabilitation of abandoned hydropower sites, adding power plants to existing non-power dams, multipurpose use, turbo-generating equipment available, and major potential problems in the area of economics and legal/institutional considerations.

LOW-HEAD HYDRO—AN EXAMINATION OF AN ALTERNATIVE ENERGY SOURCE. Compiled by John S. Gladwell and Calvin C. Warnick, University of Idaho, September 1978.

This report is a compilation of the papers delivered at the seminar, "Low-Head Hydroelectric Technology - Problems and Opportunities of an Alternative Energy Source" which was held at the University of Idaho on June 6 and 7, 1978. The papers were divided into six categories: (1) An Overview, (2) Economics, (3) Low-Head Turbines, (4) The Government Presence (5) The Environment, and (6) Surveys of Energy Potential.

IDAHO FALLS HYDROELECTRIC PROJECT, SELECTION OF UNIT SIZE, International Engineering Company, Inc., IDO-1699-2, October 1978.

The report describes the studies IECO made to select the unit size for the Idaho Falls Hydroelectric Project. The following factors were considered: water availability, estimated costs for furnishing and installing the units, the value of the power benefits established for the project, unit efficiencies, and estimated construction costs. The optimum turbine size was found to be 8.0 MW (6000 cfs discharge capacity) which would produce energy at a cost of 21 mills per kWh.

IDAHO FALLS HYDROELECTRIC PROJECT DESIGN CRITERIA, International Engineering Company, Inc., IDO-1699-1 December, 1978.

The criteria for providing a basic guide for the minimum design requirements for the civil and mechanical works of the Idaho Falls Hydroelectric Project is presented.

MICRO-HYDRO POWER: REVIEWING AN OLD CONCEPT BY TECH-
NICAL STAFF OF THE NATIONAL CENTER FOR APPROPRIATE
TECHNOLOGY, Butte, Montana, DOE/ED/01752-1, January 1, 1979.

A simple introduction to all aspects of micro-hydropower is presented,
Micro-hydropower is defined here as less than 100 kW output. A variety of
unit types are described and the many other considerations such as
economics, financing, legal, and institutional requirements are discussed. A
resource directory is included which tells where additional information may
be obtained.

COST OF CONTROLS FOR SMALL HYDROELECTRIC PLANTS OR
RIVER SYSTEMS, by P.A. Frick, and G.C. Alexander, Oregon State
University, Department of Electrical and Computer Engineering, DOE/
ET/28310-1, February, 1979.

This is a technical paper written for engineers and system scientists
familiar with hydroelectric plants and control theory. Topics addressed
(using a mathematical approach) include the following: dam dynamics, flow
control through propellor turbines, on-site head-generation control, and
complete dam (mathematical) models.

IDAHO FALLS HYDROELECTRIC PROJECT, PROJECT DEFINITION
PHASE REPORT, by International Engineering Company, Inc., IDO-
10078, February, 1979.

The results are presented for the project definition phase of the Idaho Falls
Low-Head Hydroelectric Demonstration Project. The project will result in
the redevelopment of three existing power plants on the Snake River in or
near Idaho Falls, Idaho, using bulb turbogenerators. The project is to be
partially funded by the Department of Energy. The project will demonstrate
that bulb turbine technology is an economically viable and environmentally
acceptable means of developing new or upgrading old hydropower sites.
The report also discusses benefits, costs, schedules, licensing, and financing of the project.

EXECUTIVE SUMMARIES OF SMALL/LOW-HEAD HYDROPOWER
PRDA-1706 FEASIBILITY ASSESSMENTS, EG&G Idaho, Inc., P.O. Box
1625, Idaho Falls, Idaho, May 1979.

The executive summaries of 49 of the 54 feasibility assessments performed
under DOE's Program Research and Development Announcement (PRDA)
ET-78-D-07-1706 are contained in this report.

PROCEEDINGS-SMALL/LOW-HEAD HYDROPOWER PRDA-1706
CONTRACTOR'S SYMPOSIUM, Albany, New York, May 8-10, 1979.

The report covers the remaining 5 of the 54 feasibility assessments performed under DOE's Program Research and Development Announcement (PRDA) ET-78-D-07-1706, and the presentations given at the symposium.

Special Reports:

ELI-80-8   STATE LICENSING SYSTEMS, SMALL SCALE HYDROELECTRIC PROJECTS, by Peter W. Brown, May 1980

ELI-80-11   THE PUBLIC UTILITY REGULATORY POLICIES ACT AND THE CRUDE OIL WINDFALL PROFIT TAX ACT OF 1980, Two Incentives to Small Scale Hydroelectric Development, by Peter W. Brown, June 1980

ELI-80-9   A SHORT DISCUSSION PAPER ON POSSIBLE AVENUES OF EXPLORATION OF THE RELATIONSHIPS BETWEEN SCIENCE AND TECHNOLOGY AND THE LAW, by Peter W. Brown

ELI-80-10   A TALE OF TWO FEDERAL SYSTEMS—CANADIAN-AMERICAN LAW ON HYDROELECTRIC DEVELOPMENT, by Peter W. Brown

ELI-80-16   STATE LEGISLATIVE INITIATIVES AND THE PROBLEM OF MARKETING POWER GENERATED BY SMALL POWER PRODUCERS, by Peter W. Brown, July 1980

ELI-79-47   LEGAL ISSUES INVOLVING SMALL SCALE HYDROELECTRIC DEVELOPMENT - SOME RECENT DEVELOPMENTS, Peter W. Brown, October, 1979

ELI-79-45   MAJOR LEGAL PROBLEMS IN SMALL SCALE HYDROELECTRIC DEVELOPMENT, by Peter W. Brown, June 1979

ELI-79-46   SMALL SCALE HYDROELECTRIC POWER, A PERSPECTIVE, by Peter W. Brown, August 1979

State Reports:

ELI-80-17   EXECUTIVE SUMMARY: LEGAL OBSTACLES AND INCENTIVES TO THE DEVELOPMENT OF SMALL SCALE HYDROELECTRIC POWER IN THE SIX NEW ENGLAND STATES, January 1979 (Connecticut, Maine, Massachusetts, New Hampshire, Rhode Island, Vermont), Rev. August 1980

ELI-79-9   EXECUTIVE SUMMARY: LEGAL OBSTACLES AND INCENTIVES TO SMALL SCALE HYDROELECTRIC DEVELOPMENT IN THE MID-ATLANTIC STATES, May 1979 (Delaware, Maryland, New Jersey, New York, Pennsylvania, Virginia)

ELI-79-29   EXECUTIVE SUMMARY: LEGAL OBSTACLES AND INCENTIVES TO THE DEVELOPMENT OF SMALL SCALE HYDROELECTRIC POTENTIAL IN THE SEVEN

257

VELOPMENT OF SMALL SCALE HYDROELECTRIC POWER IN PENNSYLVANIA, August 1979

ELI-80-23 LEGAL OBSTACLES AND INCENTIVES TO THE DEVELOPMENT OF SMALL SCALE HYDROELECTRIC POWER IN RHODE ISLAND, Rev. August 1980

ELI-80-24 LEGAL OBSTACLES AND INCENTIVES TO THE DEVELOPMENT OF SMALL SCALE HYDROELECTRIC POWER IN VERMONT, Rev. August 1980

ELI-79-21 LEGAL OBSTACLES AND INCENTIVES TO THE DEVELOPMENT OF SMALL SCALE HYDROELECTRIC POWER IN VIRGINIA, August 1979

ELI-79-27 LEGAL OBSTACLES AND INCENTIVES TO THE DEVELOPMENT OF SMALL SCALE HYDROELECTRIC POWER IN WEST VIRGINIA, August 1979

ELI-79-28 LEGAL OBSTACLES AND INCENTIVES TO THE DEVELOPMENT OF SMALL SCALE HYDROELECTRIC POWER IN WISCONSIN, August 1979

Federal and General Reports:

ELI-79-6 PRELIMINARY ANALYSIS OF LEGAL OBSTACLES TO THE DEVELOPMENT OF LOW HEAD HYDROELECTRIC POWER IN THE NORTHEASTERN UNITED STATES, Rev. March 1979

ELI-80-18 FEDERAL LEGAL OBSTACLES AND INCENTIVES TO THE DEVELOPMENT OF SMALL SCALE HYDROELECTRIC POTENTIAL OF THE NINETEEN NORTHEASTERN UNITED STATES, January 1979, Rev. August 1980

ELI-78-3 EXECUTIVE SUMMARY: FEDERAL LEGAL OBSTACLES AND INCENTIVES TO THE DEVELOPMENT OF SMALL SCALE HYDROELECTRIC POWER IN THE NORTHEASTERN UNITED STATES, December 1978

ELI-78-2 DAM SAFETY, EIS INTERACTION, August 1978

ELI-78-1 RECENT FEDERAL ACTION ON DAM SAFETY, August 1978

ELI-79-4 LEGAL INSTITUTIONS AFFECTING LAKE LEVEL REGULATION IN MAINE, February 1979

ELI-79-37 PROPOSALS FOR CHANGES IN THE TAXATION OF HYDROELECTRICITY, October 1979

ELI-79-44 RECOMMENDED LEGISLATIVE OPTIONS FOR IMPROVING HYDROELECTRIC DEVELOPMENT IN WASHINGTON, 1979

ELI-80-2 A HYDROELECTRIC DEVELOPMENT PLAN FOR DAMS OWNED BY THE NEW HAMPSHIRE WATER RESOURCES BOARD, Submitted to The Governor's Council on Energy, State of New Hampshire, January 1980

259

ELI-80-3   MONTANA SMALL SCALE HYDROELECTRIC DE-
            VELOPMENT POLICY REPORT: Legislative Issues and
            Options (with the National Conference of State Legislatures,
            Denver, Colorado) 1980

ELI-80-4   HAWAII SMALL SCALE HYDROELECTRIC DEVELOP-
            MENT POLICY REPORT: Preliminary Legislative Issues
            and Options (with the National Conference of State Legisla-
            tures, Denver, Colorado) 1980

ELI-80-5   SMALL SCALE HYDROELECTRIC POLICY REPORT FOR
            PENNSYLVANIA: Preliminary Issues and Options (with the
            National Conference of State Legislatures, Denver, Colorado)
            1980

ELI-80-6   SMALL SCALE HYDROELECTRIC POLICY REPORT FOR
            NEW HAMPSHIRE: Legislative Options and Recommenda-
            tions (with the National Conference of State Legislatures,
            Denver, Colorado) 1980

ELI-80-7   LEGISLATIVE OPTIONS AND RECOMMENDATIONS
            FOR FACILITATING HYDROELECTRIC DEVELOP-
            MENT IN NORTH CAROLINA, 1980

ELI-80-17   COMMENTS ON THE DRAFT REGULATIONS PROVID-
            ING FOR EXEMPTION OF SMALL HYDRO PROJECTS
            AND RELATED MATERIALS, FERC Docket No. RM80-65,
            August 1980

Case Studies:

ELI-79-31   A CASE STUDY ANALYSIS OF LEGAL AND INSTITU-
            TIONAL OBSTACLES AND INCENTIVES TO THE DE-
            VELOPMENT OF THE HYDROELECTRIC POTENTIAL
            AT GOOSE RIVER, MAINE, September 1979

ELI-79-32   A CASE STUDY ANALYSIS OF THE LEGAL AND IN-
            STITUTIONAL OBSTACLES AND INCENTIVES TO THE
            DEVELOPMENT OF THE HYDROELECTRIC POWER OF
            THE BOARDMAN RIVER AT TRAVERSE CITY, MICHI-
            GAN, September 1979

ELI-79-33   A CASE STUDY ANALYSIS OF THE LEGAL AND IN-
            STITUTIONAL OBSTACLES AND INCENTIVES TO THE
            DEVELOPMENT OF THE HYDROELECTRIC POWER AT
            THE MAXWELL LOCKS AND DAM, PENNSYLVANIA,
            September 1979

ELI-79-34   A CASE STUDY ANALYSIS OF LEGAL AND INSTITU-
            TIONAL OBSTACLES AND INCENTIVES TO THE DE-
            VELOPMENT OF THE CORNELL HYDRO PROJECT AT
            CORNELL, WISCONSIN, September 1979

ELI-79-42   EXECUTIVE SUMMARY OF THE LEGAL AND INSTITU-
TIONAL OBSTACLES AND INCENTIVES TO THE DE-
VELOPMENT OF HYDROELECTRIC POWER, A Synthesis
of Five Case Studies, 1979

Economic Reports

ELI-79-3   FUNDAMENTAL ECONOMIC ISSUES IN THE DE-
VELOPMENT OF SMALL SCALE HYDRO, January 1979

ELI-80-16   TWO ECONOMIC PAPERS: (I) MONOPSONY AND THE
SUPPLY OF POWER FROM SMALL GENERATING STA-
TIONS: (II) A PRELIMINARY ECONOMIC ANALYSIS OF
THE VALUE OF CONTRIBUTIONS BY SMALL DAMS TO
SYSTEM GENERATION RELIABILITY, November 1978,
Rev. August 1980

Public Utility Regulatory Reports

ELI-79-8   REPORT TO THE NEW HAMPSHIRE PUBLIC UTILITIES
COMMISSION: RE THE IMPLICATIONS OF THE PUBLIC
UTILITY REGULATORY POLICIES ACT OF 1978 TO
CERTAIN PROCEEDINGS BEFORE THE N. H. P.U.C.,
April 1979

ELI-79-36   COMMENTS ON THE PROPOSED REGULATIONS
UNDER SECTION 201 AND THE STAFF DISCUSSION
PAPER ON SECTION 210 OF THE PUBLIC UTILITY
REGULATORY POLICIES ACT OF 1978 - FERC Docket
No. RM79-54 and RM79-55, October 1979 Peter W. Brown &
Lawrence W. Plitch

ELI-79-40   COMMENTS ON THE PROPOSED REGULATIONS IM-
PLEMENTING SECTION 210 OF THE PUBLIC UTILITY
REGULATORY POLICIES ACT OF 1978, FERC Docket
RM79-55. December 1979

ELI-79-41   PUBLIC TESTIMONY BEFORE THE FEDERAL ENERGY
REGULATORY COMMISSION CONCERNING THE
PROPOSED REGULATIONS IMPLEMENTING SECTION
210 OF THE PUBLIC UTILITY REGULATORY POLICIES
ACT OF 1978, December 1979

ELI-80-12   PURPA SECTION 210: FINAL REGULATIONS. A Section-
by-Section Analysis. June 1980

ELI-80-13   IMPLEMENTATION OF PURPA SECTION 210: The Federal Mandates to State Regulatory Authorities, June 1980

ELI-80-14   STATE IMPLEMENTATION OF THE REGULATIONS
PROMULGATED PURSUANT TO SECTION 210 OF
PURPA: Implementation Options, June 1980

ELI-80-15 REGULATORY ISSUES PERTINENT TO THE IM-
PLEMENTATION OF SECTION 210 OF PURPA, June
1980

NPDES Reports

ELI-79-5* COMMENTS OF THE U. S. DEPARTMENT OF ENERGY
ON THE PETITION OF THE NATIONAL WILDLIFE FED-
ERATION CONCERNING THE REGULATION OF HY-
DROELECTRIC DAMS BY THE U. S. ENVIRONMENTAL
PROTECTION AGENCY PURSUANT TO THE CLEAN
WATER ACT, February 1979

ELI-79-7* MEMORANDUM OUTLINING AND DISCUSSING MAJOR
LEGAL ENVIRONMENTAL AND ECONOMIC ISSUES
RAISED BY THE PETITION OF THE NATIONAL
WILDLIFE FEDERATION TO THE U. S. ENVIRONMEN-
TAL PROTECTION AGENCY TO REQUIRE EFFLUENT
STANDARDS FOR HYDROELECTRIC DAMS IN THE
U.S., March 1979

Wind Energy Reports

ELI-79-39 LEGAL AND INSTITUTIONAL OBSTACLES TO THE DE-
VELOPMENT OF LARGE SCALE WIND ENERGY CON-
VERSION SYSTEMS IN THE STATE OF NEW HAMP-
SHIRE, November 1979

ELI-80-1 AN ANALYSIS OF THE LEGISLATIVE INITIATIVES OF
THE 96TH CONGRESS TO ACCELERATE THE DE-
VELOPMENT AND DEPLOYMENT OF WIND ENERGY
CONVERSION SYSTEMS, 1980

Conference Reports

Summary of "A CONFERENCE FOR NEW ENGLAND:
LEGAL AND INSTITUTIONAL OBSTACLES AND IN-
CENTIVES TO SMALL SCALE HYDROELECTRIC DE-
VELOPMENT," January 30-31, 1979, Boston, Massachusetts

SUMMARY OF "SMALL SCALE HYDROPOW-
ER IN THE MID-ATLANTIC STATES: RESOLUTION OF
THE BARRIERS IMPEDING ITS DEVELOPMENT," May
4-5, 1979, Washington, D.C.

Summary of "SMALL SCALE HYDROPOWER IN THE
MIDWEST: AN OLD TECHNOLOGY WHOSE TIME HAS
COME," November 14-15, 1979, Detroit, Michigan

* These reports are undergoing review and accordingly are not available at
this time.

Design Firms and Contractors with Expressed Interest in Hydropower

Acres American
Liberty Bank Building
Main At Court
Buffalo, NY 14202
(716) 853-7525

Anderson-Nichols
661 Harbour Way South
Richmond, CA 94804
(415) 237-5490

Associated Consultants, Inc.
Attn: R. E. Palmquist
3131 Fernbrook Lane North
Minneapolis, MN 55441
(612) 559-5511

Auslam & Associates, Inc.
  Economic Consultants
Attn: Margaret S. Hall
601 University Avenue
Sacramento, CA 95825

Ayres, Lewis, Norris & May, Inc.
3983 Research Park Drive
Ann Arbor, MI 48104

Banner Associates, Inc.
Attn: Joseph C. Lord
P.O. Box 550
309 South Fourth Street
Laramie, WY 82070
(307) 745-7366

Barnes, Henry, Meisenheimer & Grende
Attn: Bruce F. Barnes
4658 Gravois Avenue
St. Louis, MO 63116
(314) 352-8630

Barr Engineering Co.
Attn: L. W. Gubbe, V.P.
6800 France Avenue South
Minneapolis, MN 55435
612-0655

Bechtel National, Inc.
Attn: G. D. Coxon, Business Develop
Representative, Research Engrg.
P.O. Box 3965
San Francisco, CA 94119

Benham-Holway Powergroup
Southland Financial Center
4111 South Darlington
Tulsa, OK 74135
(918) 663-7622

Berger Associates
Attn: Richard H. Miller
P.O. Box 1943
Harrisburg, PA 17105
(717) 763-7391

Black & Veatch
Attn: P. J. Adams, Partner,
   Acting Head of Power Division
P.O. Box 8405
Kansas City, MO 64114
(913) 967-2000

Boeing Engineering & Construction
P.O. Box 3707
Seattle, WA 98124
(206) 773-8891

Booker Associates, Inc.
Attn: F. P. Eppert, V.P.
1139 Olive Street
St. Louis, MO 63101
(314) 421-1476

Bookman-Edmonston Engineering
Attn: Edmond R. Bates, P.E.
600 Security Building
102 N. Brand Boulevard
Glendale, CA 91203
(213) 245-1883

Booz, Allen & Hamilton, Inc.
4330 East-West Highway
Bethesda, MD 20014
(301) 951-2200

Bovey Engineers, Inc.
Attn: George Wallace
East 808 Sprague Avenue
Spokane, WA 99202
(509) 838-4111

Brown & Root, Inc.
Attn: C. W. Weber, Vice-Pres.
4100 Clinton Drive
P.O. Box 3
Houston, TX 77001
(713) 678-9009

Burgess & Niple, Ltd.
5085 Reed Road
Columbus, OH 43220
(614) 459-2050

Burns & McDonnell
Engineers-Architects-Consultants
Attn: J. C. Hoffman
Post Office Box 173
Kansas City, MO 64141
(816) 333-4375

Burns And Roe, Inc.
550 Kinderkamack Road
Oradell, NJ 07649
(212) 563-7700

C. H. Guernsey & Company
Attn: P. P. Pyle, Asst. Manager,
  Rocky Mountain Area
7181 Hooker Street
Westminister, CO 80030
(303) 428-5643

C.T. Male Associates, P.C.
3000 Tracy Road
Schenectady, NY 12309
(518) 785-0976

CH2M Hill, Inc.
Attn: R. W. Gillette, Director
  Of Power Generation
1500 114th Avenue, S.E.
Bellevue, WA 98004
(206) 453-5000

Chas. T. Main, Inc.
Attn: R. W. Kwiatkowski, V.P.
Southeast Tower
Prudential Center
Boston, MA 02199
(617) 262-3200

Childs & Associates
Attn: Thomas R. Childs
1317 Commercial
Billingham, WA 98225
(206) 671-0107

Clark- McGlennon Associates, Inc.
Attn: Peter Gardiner
148 State Street
Boston, MA 02109
(617) 742-1580

Clinton-Anderson Engineering, Inc.
Attn: Carl V. Anderson
13616 Gamma Road, Suite 101
Dallas, TX 75234
(214) 386-9191

Crawford, Murphy & Tilly, Inc.
Attn: Robert D. Wire
2750 West Washington Street
Springfield, IL 62702
(217) 787-8050

Curran Associates, Inc.
Attn: R. G. Curran, President
182 Main Street
Northampton, MA 01060
(413) 584-7701

Dam Divers, Division Of
 Northeast Hydro Co., Inc.
P.O. Box 127
Hudson, NH 03051
(603) 883-0020

Dames & Moore
Attn: Tim Doyle
455 E. Paces Ferry Road
Atlanta, GA 30305
(404) 262-2915

Davis Constructors & Engineers, Inc.
P.O. Box 4-2360
Anchorage, AK 99509
(907) 344-0571

DMJM Hilton
Attn: R. W. Baunach, P.E.
Suite 1111
421 S. W. 6th Avenue
Portland, OR 97204
(503) 222-3621

Ebasco Service, Inc.
Attn: R. E. Kessel, Manager
 Of Proposal Development
2 Reactor Street
New York, NY 10006

Edward C. Jordan Company
Attn: E. C. Jurick,
 Client Relations
P.O. Box 7050, Downtown Station
Portland, ME 04112
(207) 775-5401

Electrack, Inc.
Attn: A. F. Berg, Contract Manager
1925 K Street, N. W.
Washington, DC 20006
(202) 466-2543

Electrowatt Engineering Services
Attn: U. M. Buettner
1775 Pennsylvania Ave., N.W.
Washington, DC 20006
(202) 659-9553

Emery & Porter, Inc.
Attn: D. B. Emery, President
3750 Wood Street
Lansing, MI 48906
(517) 487-3789

Energy Research & Applications, Inc.
1301 E. El Segundo Blvd.
El Segundo, CA 90245
(213) 322-9302

Energy Services Consulting
37 Shoal Drive
Daly City, CA 94104
(415) 992-0700

Energy Systems Corporation
Attn: K. E. Mayo, President
One Pine Street
Nashua, NH 03060
(603) 889-5112

Engineering & Design Associates
Attn: Stanley D. Reed,
    Senior Principal
6900 Southwest Haines Road
Tigard, OR 97223
(503) 639-8215

Engineering & Power Development
    Consultants, Limited
Marlowe House, Sidcup Kent, DA15 7AU
England   01-300 3355

Engineering-Science, Inc.
Attn: G. S. Magnuson, Vice Pres.
150 North Santa Anita Avenue
Arcadia, CA 91006
(213) 445-7560

Fay, Spofford & Thorndike, Inc.
Attn: B. Campbell, Vice-President
One Beacon Street
Boston, MA 02108
(617) 523-8300

Fluid Energy Systems, Inc.
Attn: K. T. Miller,
    President/Director
2903 Ocean Park Blvd.
Santa Monica, CA 90405

Ford, Bacon & Davis Utah, Inc.
Attn: H. G. Slighting
375 Chipeta Way
P.O. Box 8009
Salt Lake City, UT 84108
(801) 583-3773

Foster-Miller Associates, Inc.
135 Second Avenue
Waltham, MA 02154
(617) 890-3200

Foth & Van Dyke Associates, Inc.
2737 S. Ridge Road
P.O. Box 3000
Green Bay, WI 54303

Geo Hydro Engineers, Inc.
Attn: Leland D. Squier, Pres.
247 Washington Avenue
Marietta, GA 30060
(404) 427-5050

Geothermal Surveys, Inc.
99 Pasadena Avenue
South Pasadena, CA 91030
(213) 255-4511

Gibbs & Hill, Inc.
Attn: E. F. Kenny, Director
  Planning & Development
393 Seventh Avenue
New York, NY 10001
(212) 760-5279

Gilbert-Commonwealth
Attn: C. A. Layland, Manager,
  Government Marketing
525 Lancaster Avenue
Reading, PA 19603
(215) 775-2600

Gutherland, Ricketts & Rindahl
Consulting Engineers, Inc.
Attn: D. R. Ricketts, P.E.
2180 S. Ivanhoe Street
Denver, CO 80222
(303) 759-0951

Halliwell Associates, Inc.
589 Warren Avenue
East Providence, RI 02914
(401) 438-5020

Hansa Engineering Corporation
Attn: Kurt A. Scholz, Pres.
500 Sansome Street
San Francisco, CA 94111
(415) 362-9130

Harding-Lawson Associates
P.O. Box 3030
San Rafael, CA 94902
(415) 472-1400

Harstad Associates, Inc.
1319 Dexter Avenue North
P.O. Box 9760
Seattle, WA 98109
(206) 285-1912

Harza Engineering Company
Attn: Leo A. Polivka,
 Group Management Director
150 South Wacker Drive
Chicago, IL 60606
(312) 855-7000

Hoskins-Western-Sonderegger, Inc.
Attn: J. M. Carpenter, Dev. Coord.
825 J Street
P.O. Box 80358
Lincoln, NE 68501
(402) 475-4241

Hoyle, Tanner & Associates, Inc.
Attn: H. D. Hoyle, Jr., President
One Technology Park
Londonderry, NH 03053
(603) 669-5420

Hydro Research Science
3334 Victor Court
Santa Clara, CA 95050
(408) 988-1027

Hydrocomp
201 San Antonio Circle
Mountain View, CA 94040
(415) 948-3919

Hydrogage, Inc.
Attn: David C. Parsons,
Hydrometric Specialist
P.O. Box 22285
Tampa, FL 33623
(813) 876-4006

Hydrotechnic Corporation
Attn: A. H. Danzberger,
 Vice-President
641 Lexington Avenue
New York, NY 10022
(212) 752-4646

International Engineering
   Company, Inc.
220 Montgomery Street
San Francisco, CA 94104
(415) 554-1200

International Engineering Company
220 Montgomery Street
San Francisco, CA 94104
(415) 544-1253

J. E. Sirrine Co. Of Virginia
P.O. Box 5456
Greenville, SC 29606
(803) 298-6000

J. Kenneth Fraser & Associates
Attn: J. K. Fraser
620 Washington Avenue
Rensselaer, NY 12144
(518) 463-4408

JBF Scientific Corporation
2 Jewel Drive
Wilmington, MA 01887
(617) 657-4170

Joseph E. Bonadiman
Attn: J. C. Bonadiman
P. O. Box 5852
606 East Mill Street
San Bernardino, CA 92412

Kaiser Engineers, Inc.
Attn: C. F. Burnap, Proj. Dev.
300 Lakeside Drive
P.O. Box 23210
Oakland, CA 94623
(415) 271-4111

Kleinschmidt & Dutting
Attn: R. S. Kleinschmidt
73 Main Street
Pittsfield, ME 04967
(207) 487-3328

Lawson-Fisher Associates
Attn: John Fisher
101 JMS Building
South Bend, IN 46601
(219) 234-3167

Livingston Associates
Consulting Geologists, P.C.
Attn: C. R. Livingston
4002 Green Oak Drive
Atlanta, GA 30340
(404) 449-8571

McGoodwin, Williams & Yates, Inc.
Attn: L. C. Yates, President
909 Rolling Hills Drive
Fayetteville, AR 72701
(501) 443-3404

Mead & Hunt, Inc.
2320 University Avenue
P.O. Box 5247
Madison, WI 53705
(608) 233-9706

Montreal Engineering Co. Ltd.
Attn: G. V. Echkenfelder, Vice Pres.
P.O. Box 777, Place Bonaventure
Montreal, Quebec, Canada H5A 1E3

Motor-Columbus Consulting Engrs.
Parkstrasse 27
CH-5401 Baden, Switzerland
(617) 875-6171

O'Brien & Gere Engineers, Inc.
Justin & Courtney Division
Attn: J. J. Williams, Vice Pres.
1617 J. F. Kennedy Blvd., Ste. 1760
Philadelphia, PA 19103
(215) 564-4282

Oscar Larson & Associates
P.O. Box 3806
Eureka, CA 95501
(707) 443-8381

Parsons Brinckerhoff
One Penn Plaza
New York, NY 10001
(212) 239-7900

Perini Corporation
Attn: R. G. Simms, Vice Pres.,
    Marketing
73 Mt. Wayte Avenue
Framingham, MA 01701

PRC Engineering Consultants, Inc.
Attn: P. N. Trumpore,
    Marketing Manager
P.O. Box 3006
Englewood, CO 80155
(303) 773-3788

Presnell Associates, Inc.
Suite 804
200 West Broadway
Louisville, KY 40202
(502) 587-9611

R. W. Beck & Associates
Attn: Richard Lofgren
200 Tower Building
Seattle, WA 98101
(206) 622-5000

Resource Planning Associates, Inc.
Attn: A. Ashley Rooney
44 Brattle Street
Cambridge, MA 02138
(617) 661-1410

Rist-Frost Associates
Attn: Fil Fina, Jr., Partner
21 Bay Street
Glens Falls, NY 12801
(603) 524-4647

Ross & Baruzzini, Inc.
Attn: Donald K. Ross
7912 Bonhomme Avenue
St. Louis, MO 63105
(314) 725-2242

Russ Henke Associates
Attn: Russ Henke
P.O. Box 106
Elm Grove, WI 53122
(414) 782-0410

Science Applications, Inc.
Attn: John A. Dracup
5 Palo Alto Square, Suite 200
Palo Alto, CA 94304
(415) 493-4326

SCS Consulting Engineers, Inc.
4014 Long Beach Boulevard
Long Beach, CA 90807
(213) 427-7437

Shawinigan Energy Consultants, Ltd.
Suite 310
33 City Centre Drive
Mississanga, Ontario, Canada L5B 2N5
(416) 272-1300

Shawinigan Engineering Corporation
Attn: James H. Cross
100 Bush Street, 9th Floor
San Francisco, CA 94104
(415) 433-7912

Sogreath Consulting Engineers
47, Avenue Marie-Reynoard
38100 Grenoble, France
(76) 09.80.22

Soil Systems, Inc.
Attn: Robert L. Crisp, Jr.
525 Webb Industrial Drive
Marietta, GA 30062
(404) 424-6200

Southern Engineering Co. Of Georgia
Attn: J. W. Cameron
Main Office
1000 Crescent Avenue, N.E.
Atlanta, GA 30309
(404) 892-7171

Stanley Consultants, Inc.
Stanley Building
Muscatine, IA 52761

Stone & Webster Engineering Corp.
Attn: J. N. White, Vice President
245 Summer Street
Boston, MA 02107

Storch Engineers
Attn: Herbert Storch
333 East 57th Street
New York, NY 10022
(212) 371-4675

Sverdrup & Parcel Associates, Inc.
Attn: D. L. Fenton, Vice President
800 N. 12th Boulevard
St. Louis, Mo 63101
(314) 436-7600

System Control, Inc.
Attn: W. H. Winnard
1901 N. Fort Myer Drive, Suite 200
Arlington, VA 22209
(703) 522-5770

Tams Engineers & Architects
345 Park Avenue
New York, NY 10022
(212) 755-2000

Terrestrial Environmental
   Specialists, Inc.
R.D. 1, Box 388
Phoenix, NY 13135
(315) 695-7228

The Kuljian Corporation
Attn: Dr. T. Mukuthoni, Vice Pres.
   Research Engineering
3624 Science Center
Philadelphia, PA 19104
(215) 243-1972

Tippitts-Abbett-McCarthy-Stratton
Attn: Eugene O'Brien, Partner
345 Park Avenue
New York, NY 10022
(212) 755-2000

Tudor Engineering Company
Attn: David C. Willer
149 New Montgomery Street
San Francisco, CA 94105

Turbomachines, Inc.
Attn: John W. Roda, President
17342 Eastman Street
Irvine, CA 92705

United Technologies Research Center
Silver Lane
East Hartford, CT 06108
(203) 565-4399

W. A. Wahler & Associates
Attn: J. L. Marzak, V.P.
1023 Corporation Way
P.O. Box 10023
Palo Alto, CA 94303
(415) 968-6250

Whitman Requardt & Associates
Attn: Henry A. Naylor, Jr.
1304 St. Paul Street
Baltimore, MD 21202
(301) 727-3450

Wilsey & Ham
1035 East Hillsdale Blvd.
Foster City, CA 94404
(415) 349-2151

Wind & Water Power
P. O. Box 49
Harrisville, NH 03450
(603) 827-3367

Woodward-Clyde Consultants
Attn: Joseph D. Boitano,
  Sr. Project Engineer
3 Embarcadero Center, Ste. 700
San Francisco, CA 94111
(415) 956-7070

Wright, Pierce, Barnes & Wyman
Attn: L. Stephen Bowers
  Vice President, Marketing
99 Main Street
Topsham, ME 04086
(207) 725-8721

Edward A. Abdun-Nur
Consulting Engineer
3067 South Dexter Way
Denver, CO 80222
(303) 756-7226

Lee Carter
Registered Professional Engineer
622 Belson Court
Kirkwood, MO 63122
(314) 821-4091

George E. Erskine
Professional Engineer
P.O. Box 3060
Eureka, CA 95501
(707) 443-6258

Mike Harper
Professional Engineer
P.O. Box 21
Peterborough, NH 03458
(603) 924-7757

Frank R. Pollock
Consulting Engineer
6367 Verde Court
Alexandria, VA 22312
(703) 256-3838

Appendix F

Hydropower
Equipment Manufacturers
and Hardware Suppliers

United States

ACEC
7308 West Rim Drive
Austin, TX 78731
Attn: Ralph J. Douglass,
        North America Coordinator

Alaska Wind and Water Power
P.O. Box G
Chugiak, AK 99566

Allis-Chalmers
Hydro-Turbine Division
East Berlin Road
P.O. Box 712
York, PA 17405
(717) 792-3511

American Ligurian Company
15 Ralsey Road South
P.O. Box 1005
Stanford, CT 06902
Attention: Dr. G.A. Cacciapuoti, President

Arbanas Industries
24 Hill Street
Xenia, OH 45385
Attention: Vilim Arbanas, President
(513) 372-1884

Axel Johnson Corporation
Spear Street Tower, Suit 445
1 Market Plaza
San Francisco, CA 94105
(415) 777-3800

Babcock & Wilcox
Power Generation Group
74 East Robinson Avenue
Barberton, OH 44203
(216) 753-4511
Attn: R. J. Harris, Marketing
    Specialist

Beckwith Electric Co., Inc.
11811 62nd Street North
Largo, FL 33543
(813) 535-3408

Boeing Engineering & Construction
P.O. Box 3707
M.S. 8C-12
Seattle, WA 98124
(206) 773-8891

Border Electric Company
Route 1
Blaine, WA 98230
(206) 332-5545

Brown Boveri Corporation
North Brunswick, NJ 08902
(201) 932-6000

Canyon Industries
P. O. Box 2543
Billingham, WA 98225

Cascade Patterns
1309 Glenwood Drive
Mount Vernon, WA 98273
Attention: George R. Maxfield
(206) 856-6608

Charmilles
EURO-USA Company
779 Barbara Avenue
Solana Beach, CA 92075
(714) 775-7974

Electric Machinery Manufacturing Co.,
  a Division of Turbodyne Corp.
800 Central Avenue
Minneapolis, MN 55413
Attention: David C. Sinclair
  Manager, Standard Products Marketing

The English Electric Corporation
500 Executive Boulevard
Elmsford, NY 10523
(914) 592-4810

General Electric Company
One River Road
Schenectady, NY 12345
Attention: C. A. Neumann,
  Hydrogeneration-marketing
(518) 385-5444

Hannon Electric Company
1605 Waynesburg Drive S. E.
Canton, OH 44707
Attention: Merrill Mossbarger
(216) 456-4728

Hydrotool Corporation
2640 Industry Way
Lynwood, CA 90262
(213) 639-4402

Independent Power Developers
P. O. Box 1467
Noxon, MT 59853
(406) 847-2315

Kvaerner-Brug A/S
c/o Kvaerner-Moss, Inc.
800 Third Avenue
New York, NY 10022
(212) 752-7310

The James Leffel and Company
Springfield, OH 45501
(513) 323-6431

Lima Electric Company
200 E. Chapman Road
Box 918
Lima, OH 45802
Attention: L. R. Thomas
(419) 227-7327

Mill Creek Hydro-Electric Co.
P.O. Box 1035
Healdsburg, CA 95448
(707) 433-2890, 2863

National Tank & Pipe Company
P. O. Box 7
10037 S. E. Mather Road
Clackamas, OR 97105
Attention: Steve McLaughlin, Sales
(503) 656-1991

Nissho-Iwai
American Corporation
Broadway Plaza
Suite 1900
700 South Flower Street
Los Angeles, California 90017
(213) 688-0600

Northeast Hydro Co., Inc.
P. O. Box 127 - Clement Road
Hudson, NH 03051

Alexis Pastuhov
P.O. Box 62
Harvard, MA 01451
(617) 456-8834

Pullman Incorporated
200 South Michigan Avenue
Chicago, IL 60604
(312) 322-7167

Pumps, Pipe and Power
Kingston Village
Autin, NV 89310

Rand Corporation
1700 Main Street
Santa Monica, CA 90406
(213) 393-0411

Short Stoppers Electric
Route 4, Box 247
Coos Bay, OR 97420
(503) 267-3559

Small Hydroelectric Systems
and Equipment
15220 S. R. 530
Arlington, WA 98223
(206) 435-3148

Sorumsand Verksted A/S
c/o Kvaerner-Moss, Inc.
800 Third Avenue
New York, NY 10022
(212) 752-7310

Sulzer Brothers, Inc.
19 Reactor Street
New York, NY 10006
(212) 425-4560

Westinghouse Electric Corp.
700 Braddock Avenue
East Pittsburgh, PA 15112
Attention: J. J. Ruffing

Foreign

Alsthom
38 Avenue Kle'ber
75784 Cedex 16
Paris, France
(1) 727.00.90

Ateliers des Charmilles SA,
109 Rue De Lyon
CH-1211 Geneva 13,
Switzerland

A. B. Bofors-Nohab
S-46101
Trollhattan
Sweden

Escher-Wyss, Ltd.
Hardstrasse 319
CH-005 Zurich
Switzerland

283

GEC Machines Limited
Large Generator Sales
Mill Road
Rugby, Warwickshire, England CV21 1BD
Telex 31671

Hitachi Ltd.
New Marie Building
Maranouchi
Chiyoda-ku,
Tokyo, Japan

Jyoti, Ltd.
Industrial Area
P.O. Chemical Industries
Barodo 390 033 India
9352, 8641 -2 -3 -4 -5

KMW
Karlstads Mekaniska Werkstad
S-681-01
Kristinehamn 1,
Sweden
(46) 550 152 00

Kvaerner Brug A/S
Box 3610
Oslo,
Norway

LMX (Leuingrad Metal Works)
KTEP (Karkov Metal Works)
V/O Energomach Exprot 35
Mosfilmovskaya
Moscow V-330
USSR

Maschinenfabrik B. Maier
4812 Brackwede
Brockhagner Strasse 14/20
Postfach 320,
West Germany

Mitsubishi Heavy Industries Ltd.
5-1 Maranoucki, 2 Chome
Chiyoda-ku
Tokyo 100
Japan

Neyrpic Department Turbines
75, Rue Feneral Margin
38100 Grenoble
France
(76) 96.48.30

Ossberger
D-8832 Weissenburg/Bay
P. O. Box 425
Weissenburg, Germany
(0 91 41) 7 90

Riva Calzoni Sp A
20144 Milan
Via Standhal 34
Italy

Sorumsand Verksted A/S
N-1920 Sorumsand
Norway
(47 2) 72 72 00

Straflo Hardstrasse 319
CH-8005
Zurich
Switzerland

OY Tampella AB
P. O. Box 267
33101 Tampere lo,
Finland

Tokyo Shibaura Electric Co., Ltd.
    (Toshiba)
Producer Goods Export Division
1-Chome, Uchisalwaicho
Chiyoda-ku, Tokyo 100
Japan

Voest-Alpine Mortan AG
Muldenstrasse 5,
A-4020 Linz
Austria

J. M. Voith, GMBH
Postfach 1940
D-7920 Heidenheim
West Germany
(0 73 21) 32 21

Canadian

Barber Hydraulic Turbine, Ltd.
Barber Point, Box 340
Port Colborne, Ontario
Canada
(416) 363-4929

Dominion Engineering Works, Ltd.
P. O. Box 220
Montreal, Quebec H3C 255
Canada
Telex 05-25168

F. W. E. Stapenhorst Inc.
285 Labrosse Avenue
Point Clair, Quebec H9R 1A3
Canada
(514) 695-2044

A Guide for Small Hydroelectric Development

This guide gives a quick look at the economics of the potential power available at a given dam site to aid in determining whether that site can provide economic hydroelectric energy. The equations and graphs included illustrate various factors to consider in evaluating a dam's hydroelectric potential. The example provided illustrates a typical hydroelectric installation.

There are two things to consider in evaluating electric power consumption: the first is the amount of power required to operate an item, and the second is how long the item is used. For example, if the power required to operate a small electric heater is 1600 watts (1.6 kW), and if the heater is operated for 3 hours per day a month (31 days), the energy consumed will be 149 kilowatt hours (149 kWh).

The following additional guidelines are given to help determine the potential use of the estimated energy.

Average home consumption	700-800 kWh/month approximately 3 kW capacity
Average consumption, totally electric home	1900 kWh/month approximately 12 kW capacity
Average commercial use	4470 kWh/month
Average industrial use	181,360 kWh/month

The above figures are typical for areas in the northern United States.

POTENTIAL CAPACITY

The potential capacity (kW) is the power output that a turbine-generator system can produce with an existing dam configuration. The general procedure for determining capacity is to establish how much water (Q) is available for diversion through a turbine and the hydraulic head (H) associated with this flow.

To determine an average potential capacity, use Fig. G-1 or the following equation:

$$kW = 0.07 \; Q_a \; H_e$$

where:

Q_a = average flow rate in cubic feet per second
H_e = effective head in feet
0.07 = constant (includes units conversion and system efficiency of 83%)

The water supply to most hydroelectric installations is not constant since most rivers, even when they have large reservoirs, are subject to periods of drought as well as periods of heavy rains and flood flows. In order to predict the power available from a particular hydroelectric site, the historical water flow records must be obtained and put in usable form. The majority of continuous flow data for a given river or stream are gathered and published by the United States Geological Survey (USGS). The most useful flow data readily available from the USGS is the average flow rate. Although hydropower equipment is usually rated at greater flow rates, the average flow rate can provide an adequate estimate for sizing the turbine on an initial, very preliminary basis. In most cases, however, the USGS can provide, on request, a flow duration curve for any given site. If the duration curve is available, the hydro plant will normally be sized for a 20 to 30 percent exceedance flow—that is, for the flow that is exceeded only 20 to 30 percent of the time. If a USGS gaging station is not located near the power plant site, reasonable approximations can be made using gaging station information, with appropriate adjustments, from a site within the same general rainfall area. The USGS will usually provide assistance in determining an approximate flow.

The gross head available at any particular site is the distance from the forebay water surface to the tailwater surface. The net effective head on the turbine is determined by deducting from the gross head the losses that are created as the water flows to the turbine and as it leaves the turbine. These losses include intake losses, penstock losses, and tailwater losses. For preliminary calculations, the intake and tailwater losses are considered negligible and are omitted. Therefore, the effective head on the turbine is the gross head less the penstock losses.

$$\text{Effective head } (H_e) = \text{gross head } (H_g) - \text{penstock}$$
$$\text{losses } (H_f)$$

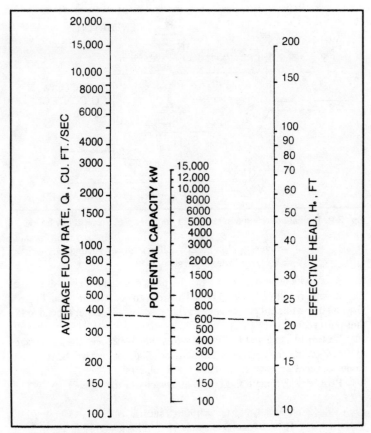

Fig. G-1. Potential capacity.

Figure G-2 illustrates a turbine installation with no inlet pipe (penstock). In this case, the effective head will equal the gross head for preliminary calculations. In Fig. G-3, where the turbine installation requires a penstock, the friction losses must be subtracted from the gross head to obtain the effective head on the turbine. Penstock losses can be determined from Fig. G-4.

Since energy losses reduce the potential capacity of the power plant, the energy lost to friction in the penstock should be kept to a minimum. This can be done by sizing the penstock for a velocity of 8 feet per second or less. The required penstock diameter can be determined, for a predetermined velocity and a given flow rate, by the following equation:

$$D = \sqrt{4Q_a/\pi V}$$

where:

D = penstock diameter in feet

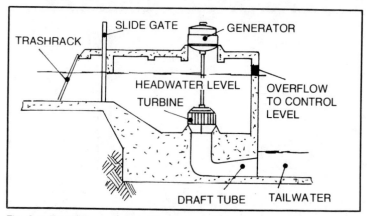

Fig. G-2. Typical open flume setting for a vertical axis turbine at low heads.

Q_a = average flow rate in cubic feet per second
V = velocity in feet per second

At a given flowrate, decreasing the penstock diameter will increase the velocity, resulting in a larger head loss due to penstock friction. Figure G-4 illustrates this effect for a velocity increase from 8 feet per second to 12 feet per second.

Example: An existing dam has a gross head of 24 feet and an average flow of 400 cubic feet per second. A penstock 800 feet long will be required to direct water through the dam to the turbine inlet.

Problem: Estimate the potential capacity of the dam.

$$Q_a = 400 \text{ ft}^3/\text{sec}$$
$$H_e = 24 \text{ ft} - [\text{penstock friction losses } (H_f)]$$

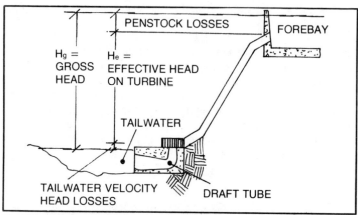

Fig. G-3. Definition sketch for a vertical axis turbine installation.

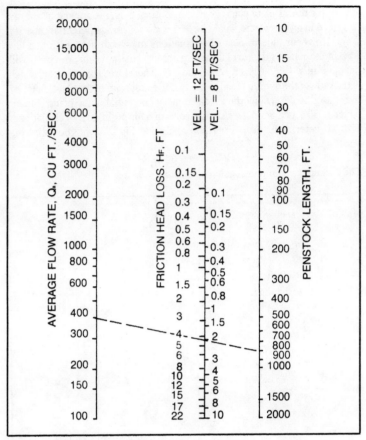

Fig. G-4. Penstock friction losses.

From Fig. G-4:

$$H_f = 2.0 \text{ ft (assuming a velocity of 8 ft/sec)}$$
$$H_e = 24 - 2.0 = 22.0 \text{ ft}$$

From Fig. G-1:

$$\text{Capacity} = 620 \text{ kW}$$

Note: Energy lost to penstock friction is $0.07 \times 400 \times 2.0 = 56$ kW, which is 9% of the potential capacity.

ENERGY POTENTIAL

The energy potential represents power (kW) operating for some time period (h). The electrical energy term generally used is kilowatt-hours (kWh). If a power plant could generate continuously, the amount of energy produced in a year's time would be 365 × 24 × average potential capacity (kW). However, due to normal fluctuations in stream flow, high and low flow limitations on the turbine, and maintenance down time, the plant will not operate at 100% capacity continuously. Therefore, a plant factor, which is the ratio of the average load to the installed capacity of the plant, must be introduced to determine the average energy potential of the plant. A plant factor of 50% is a good average figure to use for preliminary calculations.

To determine the energy potential, use Fig. G-5 or the following equation:

$$kWh = 306.60 \, Q_a \, H_e$$

The example given previously continues—

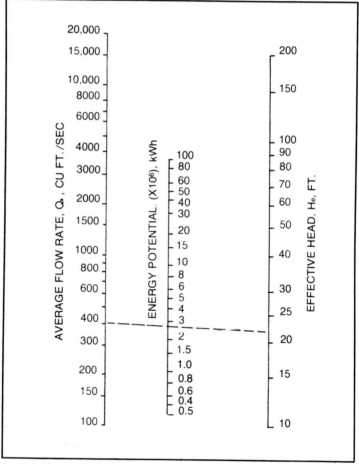

Fig. G-5. Energy potential.

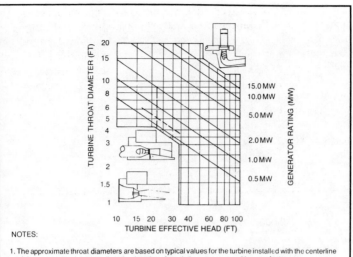

Fig. G-6. Propeller turbine throat diameters.

Problem: Estimate the energy potential of the dam.

$$Q_a = 400 \text{ ft}^3/\text{sec}$$
$$H_e = 22.0 \text{ ft}$$

from Fig. G-5:

Energy = 2,700,000 kWh

TURBINE SIZE

The approximate turbine size (throat diameter) is determined by applying the effective head (H_e) and the potential capacity (MW) to the curve in Fig. G-6.
(1000 kW = MW).

Example continued—

Problem: Determine the approximate turbine size.

$H_e = 22.0$ ft

Generator rating = 620 kW = 0.62 MW

From Fig. G-6:

Turbine Throat Diameter = 5.0 ft

ECONOMICS

Figure G-7 provides a basis for estimating the major share of construction costs for items that are governed by capacity and head, e.g., turbine, generator, and supporting electrical and mechanical equipment. The ap-

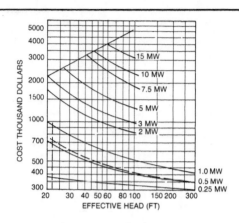

NOTES:

1. Estimated costs are based on a typical or standardized turbine coupled to a generator either directly or through a speed increaser, depending on the type turbine used.

2. Costs include turbine/generator and appurtenant equipment, station electric equipment, miscellaneous powerplant equipment, powerhouse, powerhouse excavation, switchyard civil works, an upstream slide gate, and construction and installation.

3. Costs not included are transmission line, penstock, tailrace construction, switchyard equipment, and dam modification or improvements.

4. Cost base July 1978.

5. For a multiple unit powerhouse, additional station equipment costs are $20,000 + $58,000 x (n-1), where n is the total number of units.

Source: U.S. Army Corps of Engineers, "Feasibility Studies for Small Scale Hydropower Additions," July 1979, Volume 1, Page 4-7.

Fig. G-7. Power features cost.

proximate cost of the power features can be determined by applying the effective head and the potential capacity to Fig. G-7.

Example continued—

> **Problem:** Determine estimated cost of power plant installation.
> H_e = 22.0 ft
> Generator Rating = 0.62 MU
> From Fig. G-7:
> Estimated Cost = $710,000

To determine the cost per kW, take the power features cost from Fig. G-7 and multiply by 2.0 to include the additional costs of intake works, tailrace construction, switchyard equipment, and indirect costs such as engineering; then divide by the estimated potential capacity from Fig. G-5.

$$\text{Cost/installed kW} = \frac{(2.0)\ (\text{estimated cost from Fig. G-7})}{\text{Potential capacity (kW)}}$$

The results from the above equation can now be applied to Fig. G-8 to obtain the break-even value in mills/kWh of the electrical energy generated

and used (10 mills equal one cent).
Example continued—

Problem: Determine the break-even revenue in mills/kWh

$$\$/kW = \frac{(2.0)\ (\text{estimated cost})}{\text{potential capacity}}$$

$$= \frac{(2.0)\ (\$710,000)}{620\ kW}$$

$$= \$2290/kW$$

From Fig. G-8:

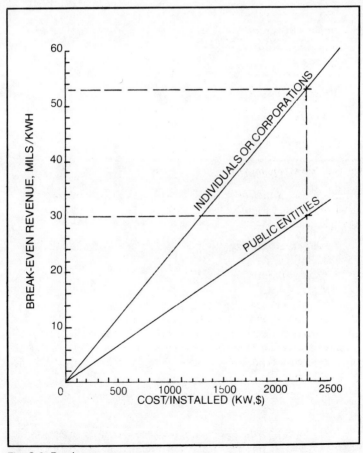

Fig. G-8. Break-even revenue.

Break-even revenue

$$= 30 \text{ mills/kWh}$$
(For a public entity)

$$= 53 \text{ mills/kWh}$$
(for an individual or corporation)

The break-even value for Fig. G-8 is the present sale price that will cover operating costs and repay the investment capital based on 30-year economic life, 8% escalation rate for revenue, 6% escalation rate for operation and maintenance expenses, and either 8% for the time value of money for public entities of 15% for the time value of money for corporations or individuals. The operating and maintenance costs were based on 3% of the total investment cost.

Glossary

Glossary

alternating current—Electrical current which periodically reverses direction.

ampere—The electrical unit of current known as the ampere is named after the French physicist André Marie Ampere, 1775-1836. Ampere taught at the Ecole Polytechnique, de Paris and is famous for his contribution to the field of electrodynamics. Electric appliances are rated either in watts, or amperes. Technically, one ampere is the amount of current which, when passed through a solution of nitrate of silver in water in accordance with certain specifications, deposits silver at the rate of 0,00118 grams per second. The watt differs from the ampere in that the watt is the amount of power expended by a current of one ampere in a resistance of one ohm.

btu—The abbreviation for British Thermal Unit, which is the amount of heat required to raise the temperature of one pound of water, one degree, Fahrenheit.

celsius—Anders Celsius was a Swedish astronomer, 1701-44. Professor of Astronomy at Uppsala. While in Paris in 1736 he was instrumental in organizing an expedition to Lapland to measure the arc of the meridian there. In 1742, he invented the centigrade, or celsius thermometer, with 100 degrees separating the freezing and boiling points of water.

cfs—cfm—Cubic feet per second, or cubic feet per minute. One cubic foot of water weighs 62.4 pounds at 62 degrees F. One Cubic Foot equals 7.48 gals. Thus cfs, or cfm denotes the volume of water or flow per second, or per minute. Note that the English, or Imperial gallon is 277.274 cubic inches, compared to 231 for the American gallon.

direct current—Current which moves in only one direction.

fahrenheit—The thermometer designed by Gabriel Daniel Fahrenheit 1686-1736, a German physicist. Fahrenheit was born in Danzig. In 1714 he conceived the idea of substituting mercury for spirits of wine in the construction of thermometers. He took as zero on his thermometric scale the lowest temperature observed by him in Danzig during the winter of 1709. The distance, or space between this point and that to which the mercury rose at the temperature of boiling water, he divided into 212 equal parts.

head—Head is the total amount of fall available. Knowledge of amount of vertical drop and the flow in cfs or cfm enables one to calculate the power available.

hertz—The frequency with which alternating current changes direction, i.e., 60 cycles a second, is called 60 Hertz, abbreviated Hz, after the German physicist Heinrich Rudolf Hertz, 1857-94, who was preeminent in the study of electromagnetic waves.

horsepower—The unit of the rate of doing work. The term originated with James Watt, who determined by experiment that a horse could do 33,000 footpounds of work per minute in drawing coal from a coal pit.

kilowatt—The common unit of electrical power. It equals 1,000 watts.

kilowatt hour—The common unit for measuring electrical energy. Ten, 100 watt bulbs, lighted for one hour, would burn 1 kilowatt hour of electricity. It is abbreviated kWh. The W is capitalized, as it stands for the proper name, Watt. This is the way utilities measure and sell electricity, by the kWh.

megawatt—A Megawatt is 100 kilowatts, abbreviated mW. A lower case "m" denotes microwatts, one thousandth of a watt.

ohm—The ohm is the unit of resistance to the passage of an electrical current through a conductor, named after the German scientist, George Simon Ohm, 1797-1854. Ohm was professor of Physics at the University of Munich from 1852. His monumental studies of electrical resistance led to what is now called Ohm's Law, which is a simple way of finding the third variable, when any two are known. The three variables are: voltage, current, and resistance.

power factor—In an alternating current system the voltage and current do not always reverse at the same instant in time. That is, they are not always "in phase." The current can be considered as being divided into two components; one in phase with the voltage and one out of phase with the voltage. The power factor of a circuit is the ratio of the in phase current to the total current, usually expressed as a percentage. Power (Watts) is the product of volts, amperes and power factor.

volt—The volt is the unit of electrical measurement named after the Italian physicist, Conte Alessandro Volta, 1745-1827. Volta was Professor of Physic's at the University of Pavia from 1779, and invented what is now known as the voltaic pile, in which a charge of electricity is created by induction. The volt is the pressure that pushes the current along the line. Think of it as analagous to pounds per square inch of pressure in hydraulics. Normal electrical pressures in use in American homes are 120 for lighting circuits, and 240 for such appliances as stoves, dryers, and water heaters. In Europe, 240 is standard. The volt is the unit of electromotive force, or emf.

watt—A unit of electrical power named after the famous Scottish inventor, James Watt, 1736-1819, Watt is also known for his work with the steam engine.

Index

Edited by Roland Phelps